Introduction to Canadian Amphibians and Reptiles

Published by the
National Museums of Canada

Coordinating Editor
Bonnie Livingstone

Editor
Penelope Williams

Production
James MacLeod

Design
BB&H Graphic Communications Limited

Typesetting
Nancy Poirier Typesetting Limited

Printing
D.W. Friesen & Sons Ltd.

Introduction to Canadian Amphibians and Reptiles

Francis R. Cook

Including a section on care of pet reptiles
and amphibians
by James A. Johnston

Illustrations by Charles Douglas
Maps drafted by Joyce Crosby Cook

National Museum of Natural Sciences
National Museums of Canada

© National Museums of Canada 1984

National Museum of Natural Sciences
National Museums of Canada
Ottawa, Canada K1A 0M8

Catalogue No. NM92-91/1984E

ISBN 0-660-10755-4

Printed in Canada

Edition française
Introduction aux Amphibiens et Reptiles du Canada
ISBN 0-660-90276-1

Canadian Cataloguing in Publication Data

Cook, Francis R. (Francis Russell)
Introduction to Canadian Amphibians and Reptiles

Issued also in French under title: Introduction aux
amphibiens et reptiles du Canada.
Issued by National Museum of Natural Sciences.
Bibliography: p.
ISBN 0-660-10755-4
DSS cat. no. NM92-91/1984E

1. Amphibians—Canada. 2. Reptiles—Canada.
3. Amphibians as pets. 4. Reptiles as pets.
I. Johnston, James A. II. Douglas, Charles III. Cook,
Joyce Crosby IV. National Museums of Canada
V. National Museum of Natural Sciences (Canada)
VI. Title.

QL654.C66 1984   597.6'0971   C83-097100-9

Contents

---

* Indicates a species that was probably introduced into Canada

---

* Indicates a species that was probably introduced into Canada

Preface

It is not difficult to justify the need for a hand-book of Canadian herpetology, the study of amphibians and reptiles, which treats under one cover all species in both groups recorded in Canada. Such a comprehensive approach has long been conspicuously lacking. Although the total number of species native to Canada is small when compared to other vertebrate groups, many amphibians and reptiles are widespread and locally abundant and are an important part of the natural environment in this country. Some kinds also tend to attract public attention and engender a spectrum of strong emotions ranging from obsessive fascination to almost pathological revulsion.

In the past decade increasing attention has been focussed on the need to conserve at least representative portions of Canadian habitats and the individual animal and plant species that are essential components of them. Amphibians and reptiles are receiving more attention with this broadening of conservation attitudes. However, partly because of their relative lack of economic importance, there is not as much accumulation of basic biological information on them in Canada as is available for other vertebrate groups. We certainly know most, if not all, the species that occur in Canada, but we have huge gaps to fill in detailed knowledge of their variations and exact distributions. Because of the lack of Canadian orientated literature on amphibians and reptiles much of our information on their habitat requirements, food, predators and reproduction is drawn from studies on populations south of our border where environmental conditions may be considerably different.

Not surprisingly, we have practically no information on fluctuation in numbers or changes in distribution in Canada. A few provincial guides exist, and some groups have been individually treated, but the most complete guides are those that cover much of the North American continent and include hundreds of southern species, a situation that can confuse the reader wanting to identify or find information only on Canadian forms, however stimulating the wider view may be.

This handbook is intended to be a comprehensive, readable but authoritative guide, providing identification and distribution maps as well as some general information on natural history. It falls between the necessarily more condensed information sheets on Canadian amphibians and reptiles distributed by the Interpretation and Extension Division of the National Museum of Natural Sciences, and the comprehensive, more technical monograph now in preparation, which will emphasize and summarize original research on Canadian amphibians and reptiles. It is not intended as a replacement for guides to individual provinces or to individual groups where, because of a more restricted topic, more detailed information can be provided. The available Canadian literature of this kind is listed on page 182, along with some of the more comprehensive treatments of North American and world amphibians and reptiles.

Common and scientific names used in this book are from the author's *Checklist of Amphibians and Reptiles of Canada* in the *Canadian Amphibian and Reptiles Conservation Society Bulletin*, December 1980. The latter follows, with a few exceptions and innovations, *Standard Common and Scientific Names for North American Amphibians and Reptiles* by J.T. Collins, J.E. Huheey, J.L. Knight and H.M. Smith, published as *Herpetological Circular*, No. 7, by the Society for the Study of Amphibians and Reptiles (1978). Totals are taken from *The Numbers of Amphibians and Reptiles* by William E. Duellman, published in *Herpetological Review*, Volume 10, Number 3, pages 83–84 (1979). French common names follow *Les noms français des amphibiens et reptiles du Canada: une liste provisoire*, by Henri Ouellet and Francis R. Cook, Syllogeus No. 32, published by the National Museum of Natural Sciences (1981).

Numerical values throughout this publication are metric in conformity with government editorial policy.

Acknowledgements

Thirty years of personal field research in Canada and the study collections of the National Museum of Natural Sciences built up under the curatorships of C.L. Patch (1913-1950), J.S. Bleakney (1952-1958) and F.R. Cook (1960 to the present) and which now exceed 98 000 specimens, provide the basis for this book. The existing literature, particularly the guides to eastern and western North America by Roger Conant and Robert C. Stebbins, has also been extensively consulted. Because of insufficient data on Canadian populations alone, maximum sizes given for most species apply to the species over the whole geographic range, not just Canadian populations.

I owe a tremendous debt to those who have influenced my interest in Canadian amphibians and reptiles both personally and through their writing: the late E.B. Shelly Logier, formerly Curator of Herpetology at the Royal Ontario Museum; J. Sherman Bleakney, formerly Curator of Herpetology at the National Museum of Canada, Natural History Branch and subsequently a professor in the Department of Biology, Acadia University (Nova Scotia); Kenneth W. Stewart, Department of Zoology, University of Manitoba; Stanley W. Gorham, head of Natural Sciences at the New Brunswick Museum; and the late G. Clifford Carl, formerly director of the British Columbia Provincial Museum. Roger Conant has been particularly kind through many years with advice and encouragement.

The active group that has maintained the Canadian Amphibian and Reptile Conservation Society, including Barbara Froom, Craig Campbell, Wayne Weller and many others, encouraged my work through the years. Many others deserve special mention including John Gilhen, Frank D. Ross, Patrick T. Gregory, R. Wayne Campbell, Robert V. Lindsay, Mike Oldham, Harold Parsons, Richard D. Ussher, William B. Preston, Dianne Secoy and the late Bruce McBride to mention only a few who have exchanged ideas and information. A legion of others have corresponded and visited the museum and provided specimens and observations. To each my debt is no less for being unable to list all their names here.

Many have been employed in the Herpetology Section and assisted in the laboratory, in the field, or undertaken their own expeditions and made major contributions in specimens and data: C.B. Powell, R. Otterdahl, R.A. Henry, M.G. Foster, F.D. Ross, W.F. Weller, D. Gordon, D. Rivard, S. Nash, A. Kozlowski, Anne M. Rick, G. Goba, S.W. Gorham, P.T. Gregory, S. Darbyshire, J.A. Johnston, F.W. Schueler, R.M. Rankin, J.P. Thonney, S. Irving, L. Jones, K. Murray, I. McMurray, K. Wong, B. Simard, A. Gracie, and R. Poole.

The National Museum of Natural Sciences has financially supported the entire project; D.E. McAllister, C.G. Gruchy and F.W. Schueler have particularly encouraged it throughout, and various chief zoologists, L.S. Russell, A.W.F. Banfield, E.L. Bousfield, W.E. Godfrey, and in its most critical late stages, H. Ouellet, have made its completion possible.

J.C. Cook, F.W. Schueler, A.K. Schueler, C.G. Gruchy, J. Gilhen, J.S. Bleakney, T.A. Huff, K.W. Stewart, P.A. Gregory and D. Green have read earlier versions in whole or part and provided extensive useful comments and corrections, although they are not to be held responsible for the final text.

James A. Johnston, formerly curatorial assistant in the Herpetology Section of the National Museum of Natural Sciences, wrote the care in captivity section and aided in many aspects of the work.

Charles Douglas has been painstaking in preparing the illustrations, largely under the most difficult conditions, from preserved specimens.

Joyce Crosby Cook has made a larger contribution than anyone else over 22 years at the museum, in the field and at home, collecting, preserving, examining specimens and discussing all aspects of the work. Her assistance and encouragement pervade the result throughout. She has also prepared all the distribution maps.

The final copy was only possible through the efforts of Bonnie Livingstone, Louise L. Trahan and Penelope Williams whose editorial talent and diplomacy have been of inestimable assistance.

Francis R. Cook

Introduction to Amphibians and Reptiles

Diversity and Classification of Animals

Estimates of the number of kinds (species) of animals in the world are difficult to make and frequently revised. From the rate at which new species are still being discovered and described by scientists it is obvious that the task is far from completed. One recent estimate sets the total at 1 120 000, but others are much higher, between two and four million!

Scientists have divided these kinds according to a system of classification first used for the entire animal world in 1758 by the Swedish naturalist, Karl von Linné (usually referred to by the Latinized version of his name, Carolus Linnaeus). Each distinct kind of animal is designated by two Latin words; the first is the genus (plural, genera) and the second is the species. Somewhat confusingly these words together are referred to as the "species name". In zoology, the first letter of the genus is always capitalized, whereas the species is never capitalized. (Botanists previously capitalized the first letter of a species word if it was derived from a proper name but this practice is now disappearing in botany and has long been discarded in zoology for the sake of uniformity.) Sometimes a third word, for a subspecies, is added to indicate a distinct geographic race of the species. The same Latin species word may be used with different genus words but each combination of genus and species must be unique and apply to only one kind of animal. It is permissible for this combination to duplicate a plant name, but this is discouraged.

Higher categories are also used: similar genera are grouped into *families*, families into *orders*, orders into *classes* and classes into *phyla* (singular, phylum). Subfamilies, suborders, etc. are used when additional subdivisions of classification are needed.

One major phylum of animals is Chordata, animals that at some stage in their life history have a rod-like structure called a notochord down the back. This characteristic distinguishes them from all other phyla of animals such as Mollusca (snails and clams, etc), Echinodermata (starfish, sea urchins, etc.), Annelida (earthworms, leeches, etc.), Arthropoda (insects, spiders, crabs, etc.) and many others often referred to collectively as invertebrate animals. The phylum Chordata is composed of several small subphyla of marine animals, and one large subphylum—the Vertebrata, animals with a segmented or vertebrated backbone of cartilage or bone, including *Homo sapiens*, so-called reasoning man.

Vertebrata consist of about 37 438 species, about three per cent or less of the total species of world animals. Fishes (comprised of several classes), amphibians, reptiles, birds and mammals (one class each) are the major divisions of this subphylum.

Few people have trouble in recognizing most fish, or any bird or mammal, as a member of its group. However, amphibians and reptiles are often confused. The technical aspects of their classification involve a detailed knowledge of their skeletons and the comparative features of these in fish, birds and mammals. Since we know little of fossil kinds of vertebrates except their skeletons, these have become the most important characters for defining major groupings, even in still existing species.

In the fossil record, legless, gilled fish appeared first, followed by amphibians, reptiles, warm-blooded, feathered birds, and haired and milk-producing mammals. All these groups have coexisted for a long time, while various lines within them have expanded at different periods. Some major divisions (orders) of both amphibians and reptiles thrived millions of years ago, but have left no living likeness of themselves. The two orders of dinosaurs are the most familiar examples of such extinct groups.

The impression is often given, because of the number of extinct lines, that existing amphibians and reptiles are merely evolutionary relics in a world now dominated by birds and mammals. However, the frogs, snakes and lizards, with 2770, 2267 and 3307 species respectively, are definitely successful and diverse animals at the present time, judged both by the local abundance of many of their species and by the comparative number of species of birds (9031) and, particularly, of mammals (3993).

Amphibians and reptiles might appear less important now because of the superficial similarities among many species, particularly within frogs and within snakes, and the relative inconspicuousness of the majority of species in size, habits or both. Other factors are that mammals are more interesting to humans because they have greater similarities in structure and requirements to that of the observer, and birds attract more attention because they are so often flagrantly showy and therefore attractive in colour and vocalizations. Both mammals and birds have also been more economically important to humans: neither amphibians nor reptiles have been as extensively depended upon as a source of food, clothing or decoration, particularly in western cultures. In fact, they have often been regarded primarily as repulsive or distasteful perhaps because of their lack of perceived usefulness or because they frequently thrive in damp insect-infested habitats that often are considered unhealthy for humans. Their importance in the ecological sense, as consumers and consumed, must not however be underrated; they are among the most abundant forms of vertebrate life.

One characteristic common to both amphibians and reptiles is their relative inability to control their body temperature internally. They are described as "cold-blooded," or poikilothermic and ectothermic as contrasted to the "warm-blooded," homeothermic or endothermic condition of birds and mammals. Of these terms, *cold-blooded* and *poikilothermic* are now often considered inappropriate because they both convey the impression of consistently lower body temperatures. Amphibians or reptiles are not always much colder than birds or mammals, and not all birds and mammals maintain uniformly constant body temperatures. The terms *ectothermic* and *endothermic* are gaining wide usage because they denote the contrast between the major heat source, external or internal respectively.

Many amphibians and reptiles function best at relatively high body temperatures; warmth is essential for internal functions such as digestion and excretion, and for alertness and general activity. Although there is great variation among groups, these animals are not helplessly dependent on the air or water temperature surrounding them, and do not necessarily maintain the same temperature as their environment. They use a number of strategies to maintain a preferred temperature. One is to alternate between basking in the direct sun and sheltering in shaded areas. Some species have a fine sense of timing that allows precise maintenance of a fairly constant preferred temperature for extended periods if the environment provides a gradient of temperature to choose from.

At least a few species can raise their body temperatures above their surroundings by retaining internal heat produced by muscle contraction. An Indian Python coiled around its eggs was found to be 4.7°C warmer than its surroundings, and a Leatherback Turtle maintained a temperature of 18°C above the 7.5°C temperature of the sea water around it.

However, the general activity and overall distribution of amphibians and reptiles is correlated with fluctuations in external temperature and climate. The inactivity produced by low temperatures is not a complete liability, and these animals should not be dismissed as inferior to birds and mammals because of it. There are situations where such inactivity may be an advantage rather than a disadvantage. They are not obligated constantly to seek food just for the sake of maintaining body heat, a necessity normally imposed on birds and mammals. Neither do amphibians and reptiles have to expend energy on long migrations or in growing protective coats of hair or feathers. During cool periods, or in the winter, lowered temperatures put them on a bare maintenance schedule where food is not required and oxygen requirements are minimal. This allows them to utilize efficiently food sources that are seasonal rather than depending on the availability of year-round sources. Most of their activity, and therefore their need for energy, can be concentrated on courtship, mating and the production of the next batch of eggs or sperm. However, extreme fluctuations in climate, such as unusually severe winters or abnormally cool summers or extremes of rainfall and drought, do have an effect on their distribution and abundance. Food, predators, parasites and other factors are probably less important in regulating amphibian and reptile numbers than the vagaries of climate, at least in temperate regions.

The technical aspects of classification of amphibians and reptiles are available from textbooks on herpetology or in general books on vertebrates. Here amphibians and reptiles are contrasted on the basis of some readily observable characteristics of existing forms.

Characteristics of Amphibians

Most amphibians have scaleless, usually moist skins and include the well-known frogs, the less well-known salamanders (lizard-like in general form, but unlike lizards in having a scaleless skin), and the little-known, tropical caecilians (worm-like in form, and the only amphibian group which includes some species with small scales embedded in the skin). Amphibians typically lay eggs protected only by a thick layer of jelly, though in a few salamanders and frog-like species the young may be born alive. The phrase, "born alive," redundant in its literal context, is used to describe young that are free-living from the moment they leave their parent in contrast to the living young laid as a developing egg that has to complete its term as an embryo after it has left its mother's body. Many amphibians lay their eggs in water, in ponds, streams and similar habitats; the young hatch as gilled larvae and live in the water until they transform as lung-possessing air-breathers. Some, including a large group of tropical frogs and many salamanders, lay large-yolked eggs in moist, protected places on land; the young usually complete the larval stage in the egg and hatch as miniatures of the parent.

In most frogs fertilization, the union of sperm and eggs, occurs outside the female as the egg is being laid. The males usually have a distinctive breeding call. Canadian species typically congregate in breeding groups where the males, calling together, produce a chorus that may attract females and other males to their site. In most salamanders fertilization is internal. The males perform a courtship display to determine if the female is receptive and to entice her to pick up with her cloaca a packet of sperm, or spermatophore, which the male has deposited.

Amphibians appear defenceless, although salamanders and most frogs have small low teeth. None have claws or spines. However, many amphibians have poisonous or highly distasteful skin secretions which other animals find noxious or toxic. Elaborate warning postures are displayed and bright signal colorations occur in some kinds. Many, particularly salamanders, depend on secretive behaviour, staying beneath the ground or under leaves, logs, stones or similar cover much of the time. Protective colour, patterns that blend in with their habitat, and a "freezing" behaviour are aids in escaping detection. If discovered, most frogs are capable of rapid leaps, especially the long-legged frogs, which can leap rapidly, suddenly and with a random change in direction to add to the confusion of a predator. Even some salamanders, when discovered, are capable of an astonishingly rapid wriggle that often places them under new concealment before a potential predator has had time to focus on them.

Characteristics of Reptiles

Reptiles, in contrast to amphibians, have well-protected skins, usually covered completely by scales. These scales may be relatively small, where flexibility is important (as in the snakes and lizards, and in the limbs of turtles), or large, covering a rigid bony protective structure (as in the shells of turtles). Since reptiles have few skin glands, their skins are dry when out of water, though many smooth-scaled forms have a polished shiny look that may appear slimy to anyone who hasn't actually touched one.

Fertilization is internal in reptiles. Males have well-developed copulatory organs. In snakes and lizards these are paired and called *hemipenes*, while turtles and crocodilians have a single penis, and the tuatara doesn't have any at all. The hemipenes of snakes are covered with spines, which may compensate for the lack of appendages to hold the female during mating. All reptiles lay shelled eggs on land, never in the water, or bear fully developed young. This frees them to a large extent from the amphibian dependence on water or moist environments, but still their eggs must be protected from extremes of dampness or dryness.

Although external heat is vital for egg development, excessive heat or cold will kill eggs. Most turtles lay their eggs in sand or earth where sufficient moisture and heat are available to incubate them in the summer. Lizards and snakes place their eggs in the interior of rotting logs, under stones, or even in manure piles. Some species of lizards, snakes and crocodilians stay with their eggs to guard them from small predators. Turtles, however, carefully cover the nest site to make it inconspicuous, but here their obligation ends—they abandon the area leaving the clutch to the fortunes of the weather and chance discovery by predators. Raccoons and skunks often detect these nests and excavate the eggs for a meal.

In turtles, crocodilians and the tuatara (a primitive lizard-like reptile, which exists now only on islands off New Zealand and is the sole survivor of the order Rhynchocephalia) all species lay eggs. The more modern reptiles, the Squamata (lizards and snakes) have evolved many species that essentially carry the eggs inside the female until their development is completed and they "hatch" at their birth from their mother. This procedure seems to have occurred independently in many lines since many subgroups contain both egg-laying and live-bearing species. After birth few reptiles (some crocodilians are a notable exception) remain with their young, but these young are fully capable of responding to all the necessary clues for food-searching and defence that form the essential reactions for survival.

Reptiles are much better equipped to defend themselves than amphibians. Not only does their scaly skin or, in the case of turtles, bony armour, afford better protection, but they often have sharp teeth or beaks capable of inflicting wounds, and limbed individuals usually have claws. Some snakes and two lizards, which occur in the southwestern United States and Mexico, have evolved venom and usually specialized fangs for injecting it. The poison-producing glands are modified from salivary glands of the mouth. One function of venom may be to initiate digestion of prey before it reaches the predator's stomach. Stronger venom that immobilized or killed prey may have been a later development. The use of poison in defence is accompanied by threatening behaviour and often conspicuous patterns. For defence a mild poison can be as useful as a powerful one: a poison that causes severe pain but does not kill teaches the attacker to avoid similar snakes in future. Certainly a bite from even the most potently venomous snake does not invariably kill all larger animals.

Diversity and Distribution of Amphibians and Reptiles

There are some 3260 recognized kinds of amphibians in the world today, divided among three orders: Gymnophiona (caecilians) 154; Caudata (salamanders) 336; and Anura (frogs and toads) 2770. There are 5954 recognized kinds of reptiles divided among four orders: Testudines (turtles) 222, Rhynchocephalia (tuatara) 1, Squamata (lizards, amphisbaenids and snakes) 5709 and Crocodilia (alligators and crocodiles) 22. In Canada, only 85 species of amphibians and reptiles are recognized, and three of these may have been introduced. The low number of native species, 82, emphasizes that the great diversity of the group is in the tropics and subtropics, and that the northern regions are depauperate in species. Even within Canada, this progressively diminishing diversity can be seen as one moves from south to north. Most Canadian species are restricted to the southern portions of the country, with the greatest number of forms occurring in southwestern Ontario and southwestern British Columbia.

The tree line marks the end of cold tolerance for Canadian amphibians; the reptiles drop out before this point is reached. No species ranges into the vast northern tundra of Canada beyond the forest. The Wood Frog does cross the Arctic Circle, but only within the shelter of the wooded valley of the Mackenzie River of the Northwest Territories. Though sparse in species, northern regions often have very large populations of the few species that do thrive there, and these species form an important part of the dynamic interrelationships of life both as predators and as prey.

Amphibians and reptiles are often an important element of the life of seasonal habitats, particularly temporary ponds formed by spring melt-water or heavy rains. Many amphibians have very high reproductive rates that allow them to recover rapidly from the ecological disasters which such habitats are prone to (i.e. rapid drying in arid years) and to recolonize such habitats in more favourable years.

There are also major east-west differences in the amphibians and reptiles present in Canada. A basic division can be made into eastern, central and western regions. The boundary between eastern and central regions is the abrupt transition in eastern Manitoba between the eastern Boreal Forest and the Aspen Parkland and prairie. The boundary between central and western regions lies along the eastern edge of the foothills of the Rocky Mountains in western Alberta.

The eastern region has deciduous forest in its southern extremity in southwestern Ontario, the central region has short-grass prairie, and the western has prairie in the narrow valleys of central British Columbia and rain forest along the coast. All three regions have boreal forest in their central and northern portions. Various transitions occur between southern and northern regions: the Great Lakes and acadian forests in the eastern region, aspen parkland in the central region, and varying montane associations in the rugged topography of the western region.

The eastern region contains the greatest number of species, generally adapted to the widespread availability of lakes, ponds, marshes and forests. The central region is characterized by fewer species, many of these adapted to arid prairie conditions. The western region is intermediate in species numbers and has arid adapted species in the southern interior valleys, and species that require more moist conditions in the coastal area.

Order Caudata
Salamanders and Newts

There are approximately 336 species of "tailed amphibians" or salamanders in the world. Eight families are usually recognized: seven of these occur in North America, four of which range into Canada.

The English term *salamander* originated from the European *Salamandra* (family Salamandridae) from a Greek word meaning "a lizard-like animal." The European Salamander was credited in ancient times with an ability to endure fire and extreme heat, and the word *salamander* has since been applied to cooking utensils and other objects that can withstand high temperatures. The connection between the relatively delicate, moisture-loving animal and the conditions it would seek most to avoid was probably erroneously reached. When logs into which salamanders had taken cover were thrown into a fire, the amphibian would, naturally, make a desperate dash to escape. If its progress had been rapid enough it would emerge from the fire unscathed. The conclusion that the salamander actually preferred to live in fire may have been based on such fortuitous escapes.

In England, only the partly aquatic members of the family Salamandridae occur, and the words *newt* and *eft* of Anglo-Saxon origin are used. The Anglo-Saxon word, "Efete," or "evete," became "ewt" in medieval England and "an ewt" eventually came to be "a newt." Generally, newt applies only to these members of Salamandridae, whereas salamander is applied to the rest of the family and all other species in the order.

Fertilization is internal in all but two families of Salamanders, neither of which occur in Canada. After a period of courting the female to establish that she is receptive, the male deposits a packet or "spermatophore," which consists of a gelatinous base with a clump of sperm above. This sperm cup is picked up by the courted female with the lips of her cloaca (vent) and is retained inside her body until the eggs are laid.

In contrast to frogs, salamanders are largely silent, though some species produce a few low sounds – perhaps to establish their territory. The loud mating calls used by frogs for species recognition are replaced in salamanders by elaborate courtship movements by the male, which precede fertilization.

Aquatic salamander larvae always have external gills and, in contrast to frog tadpoles, their front legs are visible first, followed by the later appearance of the hind limbs. They are carnivorous in contrast to the mainly vegetarian habits of tadpoles.

Salamanders inhabit a variety of streams, rivers, ponds, lakes, seepage areas and moist woodlands. Only one species (the Tiger Salamander) occurs in the dry prairie and aspen parkland of central Canada. Canadian species represent a diversity of size and life history, from the large, permanently gilled, aquatic Mudpuppy to the small, lungless, woodland plethodontids, which live in damp forests.

Family Proteidae
Mudpuppy

Mudpuppy
Necture tacheté
Necturus maculosus
This is the most unusual salamander in Canada. It belongs to a small family, Proteidae, which is represented in Europe only by the cave-dwelling, unpigmented Olm, *Proteus*, and in eastern North America by the five species of *Necturus*.

Necturus is permanently aquatic, with a stout body and limbs with four toes on each foot. (Most salamanders have five toes on each hind foot and only four on each front one.) The Mudpuppy is a muddy brown or grey-brown above as an adult. It is marked with black spotting and a narrow band of dirty white or grey along the belly. Most conspicuous are the feathery deep-red external gills that fluff out on each side of the head. Unlike most other salamanders, Mudpuppies retain these gills throughout their lives; there is never a transformation to an air-breathing, gill-less adult. The head is markedly flattened, and the tail is short and strongly laterally flattened. Adult Mudpuppies may attain a total length of over 300 mm; a maximum size of 486 mm has been recorded. Mudpuppies exceed even the western races of the Tiger Salamander and the Pacific Giant Salamander in claiming the title of being Canada's largest salamanders. The young Mudpuppy is black with longitudinal yellow stripes. With the approach of maturity they gradually change to the adult colour.

Mudpuppies are found in southern Quebec and Ontario and in northwestern Ontario and southern Manitoba. They live in rivers, some large lakes, and in lower reaches of tributary creeks that do not become intermittent or dry up in the summer months. They are rarely seen, but both the adults and the yellow-striped juveniles may occasionally be discovered under flat rocks in shallow water, and the adults are sometimes taken on a hook and line by fishermen. This most frequently occurs during ice fishing, particularly in the late winter. The uninitiated may greet such a catch with great astonishment and be certain that they

Necturus maculosus

have captured a "missing link," "living fossil" or a "fish with ears and legs," and be surprised to learn that such an apparently bizarre life-form could be well known to local scientists.

Courtship and mating are thought to take place in the fall. The following spring the female excavates a nest cavity under stones, logs or similar objects at water depths of 10 to 150 cm. Clutches ranging from 18 to 180 eggs have been recorded for the species, though the variation in the number of eggs laid by Canadian populations is unstudied. The eggs have variously been reported to be from 5 to 11 mm in diameter and hatch in four to eight weeks into larvae ranging from 20 to 25 mm in length. The female apparently may stay with the eggs throughout their incubation period, remaining in a downstream-facing entrance to the excavation where the eggs have been deposited. It has been reported that it takes five years for an individual to attain sexual maturity. First breeding is thought to occur at about 200 mm in length.

The Mudpuppy eats a variety of aquatic organisms. Studies have shown that crayfish are a major item, comprising 38% of the volume of stomach contents; insects (17%), fish (12%) and snails (7%) are other animal life eaten. Plants comprised 18% of stomach contents but some of this material may have been swallowed accidentally when animals were being eaten; sticks accounted for another 4%.

Family Salamandridae
Newts

This widespread family includes the typical salamanders and the newts of Europe, Asia and North Africa. It is represented in North America only by newts; one genus *Notophthalmus* is found on the eastern half of the continent, and another, *Taricha*, occurs in western North America. In all, about 43 species and 14 genera are included in the world distribution of the family.

The newts of eastern North America *(Notophthalmus)* are relatively small and often partly or wholly aquatic as adults, but between the larval stage and maturity they usually have a terrestrial stage (the eft), which may last one to three years. Western newts *(Taricha)* are larger, more robust in build and often largely terrestrial outside the breeding season. The vertical costal grooves, which are prominent on the sides of Canadian salamanders between front and hind legs, are indistinct in newts.

The food of newts includes a variety of insects and other invertebrates such as leeches, worms and small crustaceans and molluscs. Their skins contain glands that secrete tetrodotoxin, a compound that is lethally toxic in small quantities to most animals. Tetrodotoxin is particularly abundant in the skin, viscera and eggs of *Taricha*, but is also found in *Notophthalmus* skin secretions, particularly in the eft stage. This may serve to discourage many would-be predators. Garter snakes (particularly *Thamnophis sirtalis*) seem to be able to eat even western newts without ill effects.

Newt courtship is elaborate, and visual recognition, smell and touch may all be used by a male in enticing a female to pick up the spermatophore he eventually deposits. The eggs in both eastern and western species in Canada are deposited singly along submerged plant stems.

One widespread northern representative of each of the two North American genera occurs in Canada.

Eastern Newt
Triton vert
Notophthalmus viridescens

This eastern species attains a maximum length of about 140 mm. It generally has a well-marked terrestrial phase (eft) following transformation. These rough-skinned, small editions of the adults are brown to brick red, usually with a row of black-circled red spots on each side. After a variable period of one to three years they reach maturity and return to ponds or lakes to breed. Where these newts inhabit permanent water, the maturing adults change their ground colour to green, finely marked with tiny black dots, which may outline a light dorsal stripe. There is a prominent dark stripe through the eye. The spots remain red and stand out on this background, and the underside becomes bright yellow, marked with a profusion of black dots.

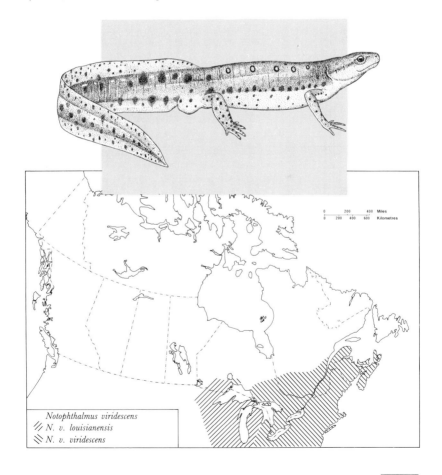

Notophthalmus viridescens
/// *N. v. louisianensis*
\\\ *N. v. viridescens*

There are also changes in form with the resumption of aquatic life; a broad median fin develops above and below the tail, which is most exaggerated in males. The hind legs of males are somewhat enlarged and the inner surfaces and toe-tips have horny black areas. Newts that breed in temporary ponds often do not achieve the bright colours or fin development of those that breed in permanent ponds and lakes, and tend to remain brown or dull olive-green. They become terrestrial again in the summer if the level of the ponds is severely reduced. In northwestern Ontario, some populations not only omit the terrestrial eft stage but may contain neotenic individuals, which attain adult coloration and sexual maturity while still retaining their gills.

This newt is widespread in eastern Canada from Prince Edward Island to northwestern Ontario. It is most abundant in lakes and bog ponds in Cape Breton Island and the Gaspé where there are few fish competitors. Two poorly defined subspecies have been recognized in Canada: the Red-spotted Newt, *Notophthalmus viridescens viridescens*, and the Central Newt, *N. v. louisianensis*. These races may intergrade (interbreed to produce populations with characters intermediate between them) along the north side of Lake Superior. The western race is characterized by smaller size, more slender build, and the absence of red spots. However, some populations of the eastern race in Prince Edward Island, Cape Breton and the Gaspé also contain many unspotted individuals. The normal range of spots in the eastern race number two to seven on each side, but extreme individuals with 46 and 64 red spots in total have been recorded in Canada.

Roughskin Newt
Triton rugueux
Taricha granulosa
This western species is characterized by a generally rough, granular skin, though breeding males have relatively smoother skins. Its colour ranges from plain dark brown to tan above and yellow to orange below. It has no spots and is relatively large, attaining a total length of 178 mm. It is common in western British Columbia, especially on Vancouver Island, and is found north into coastal Alaska. The Roughskin Newt breeds in ponds and small lakes. On land it takes cover under logs, rocks or forest litter generally in damp places but can sometimes be found crawling in the open during the daytime. At some localities adult newts may be aquatic through much of the summer, particularly in the northern portion of their range and at high altitudes. In Alaska the larvae have been reported to take two years to develop to transformation. Since there is no colour difference between recently transformed young and mature adults, the term *eft* has not been used.

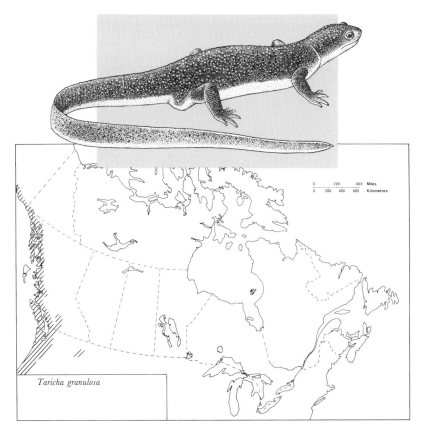

Taricha granulosa

The mass migrations of western newts to their breeding ponds after the adults have been widely dispersed in the non-breeding season has been intensively studied in a related species in California, and a well-developed ''homing'' ability has been demonstrated. These animals assume an exaggerated defence posture if attacked, bending the body with the head and tail thrust upward to show the bright colour of the underside. This has been termed ''unken'' posture by behaviourists, and is also shown by the Eastern Newt, particularly in the eft stage. It may serve to expose better the bright colours that may warn the attacker of its toxic properties.

Family Ambystomatidae
Mole Salamanders

This family of chunky, largely terrestrial salamanders is restricted to North America and consists of four genera, containing 33 species. Two genera with eight species are represented in Canada. Most species are secretive throughout much of the year, living in leaf litter, under stones and logs, or in burrows of other animals, hence the group name, "mole salamanders." They are most often seen at the surface during and after heavy rains, particularly after dark. All the seven Canadian species of *Ambystoma* breed in the early spring, generally as soon as the snow melts. Large migrations to temporary ponds, ditches and shallow edges of lakes may occur on rainy nights at this time. They may be seen for these few weeks during the breeding period only after dark when a headlamp or flashlight will often reveal them crossing roads and other open areas, or on the bottom of ponds and ditches. The very fortunate and patient observer may even glimpse the courtship of a pair.

Mole salamanders either lay their eggs in shallow water singly or in small clusters (as in *Ambystoma laterale*) or in moreor-less globular masses (as in *Ambystoma maculatum* and most other species). The eggs hatch in a few days to a week depending on the pond temperature. In *Dicamptodon* the stream-living larva has reduced gills and fins, but in *Ambystoma* the larva is of the pond type. The latter are chunky little animals with relatively large external gills and well-developed tail fins that extend forward along the back to the neck. They are variously patterned and difficult to identify as to species. The number of "rakers" (finger-like projections) on each arch of the external gills will separate some forms, but these rakers become more conspicuous with age, making comparison of counts from small and large larvae difficult. At hatching the larvae have only front legs but the limb buds for the hind ones soon appear and develop. This order is the reverse of frog tadpoles whose hind legs appear first. Larvae of mole salamanders are carnivorous and voracious. They devour a variety of aquatic invertebrates small enough for them to swallow, and larger larvae will also eagerly eat smaller larvae.

Transformation generally occurs in July or August, depending on the size of the pond and the relative warmth of the particular year. After transformation the young salamanders quickly disperse from the pond. However the larvae of at least two Canadian species, the Tiger Salamander and the Northwestern Salamander, may remain in the breeding waters over winter. These larvae grow to a large size and in some localities become sexually mature without losing their gills. This process is called *neoteny*, reproductive maturity with the retention of some immature characteristics. The gilled, aquatic neotenous Tiger Salamanders are sometimes called "mudpuppies" on the prairies, but they are distinctive in form and coloration from the eastern true Mudpuppy, *Necturus maculosus*. Neotenous Tiger Salamanders can be induced to transform into terrestrial adults, but *Necturus* has lost this ability completely. One quick distinguishing character is the number of hind toes: *Ambystoma* (except for small larvae) always have five toes on each hind foot; *Necturus* always has four. Neotenous Tiger Salamanders of longer than 300 mm have been recorded.

On the prairies at least, transformation may be synchronized with rainfall. Heavy summer rains may bring huge numbers of transformed and transforming young salamanders, with tiny gill stubs still not completely resorbed, migrating out of the ponds. Where such a migration crosses a highway the death toll from traffic can be immense. However it is questionable that it has ever reached the legendary state claimed by some westerners that cars have to use winter chains on the tires to get through the slippery mess.

Adult mole salamanders are usually as voracious as their larvae and eat a variety of invertebrates. The huge *Dicamptodon*, the Pacific Giant Salamander, which has been recorded as long as 305 mm, occasionally eats small mammals such as deer mice and shrews.

Identification of transformed members of the family can usually be made from coloration alone or from their location. For example, a west-coast species would not be expected in eastern Canada, but range extensions may be found within any general region since the complete distribution is probably not yet known for many species. All mole salamanders have more-or-less prominent vertical costal grooves along the sides, corresponding to the number of muscle segments, and hence ribs. The usual method of counting the grooves between the front and hind leg gives a lower count than the actual rib number since some ribs are situated over, or immediately before or after, the limb girdle, and their grooves are often not conspicuous.

The Jefferson Salamander Complex

The most confusing forms in the genus *Ambystoma* are found in the Jefferson Salamander complex. These are small to medium-sized salamanders, with adults ranging from 102 to 178 mm in total length. They are brown, grey or black above and usually have conspicuous bluish markings over the sides, lower sides and belly. This complex is comprised of the Blue-spotted and Jefferson salamanders, which are described below.

Before 1954, one species was recognized under the name Jefferson Salamander (named for Jefferson College, rather than for a person). Then it was discovered that two distinct forms existed; the more southerly ranging of these retained the name Jefferson Salamander *(Ambystoma jeffersonianum)* while the more northerly one was designated the Blue-spotted Salamander *(Ambystoma laterale)*. A decade later, extensive interbreeding between these species was documented. The resulting hybrids were found to be triploid, that is they have three sets of chromosomes (for a total of 42) whereas both the Jefferson and Blue-spotted Salamanders had only two sets (for a total of 28 each). These triploid hybrids were found to occur over a broad geographic area overlapping the northern range of the Jefferson Salamander and the southern edge of the Blue-spotted Salamander.

Initial studies indicated that triploids were almost always female, and were courted and took sperm from diploid males of the species with which they occurred. Although the penetration of this sperm into the egg was necessary to initiate egg development, the sperm itself did not contribute to the individual salamander that developed from the egg; the resulting individual was triploid with only chromosomes from its mother. In addition, two types of triploid were identified; a more southern type, breeding with *A. jeffersonianum* which had two sets of *A. jeffersonianum* chromosomes and one set of *A. laterale* chromosomes, and a northern type, breeding with *A. laterale*, which had the reverse. It was then suggested that because neither triploid form took any contribution from its male "parent" that each was now separate from the diploid forms, and each should be recognized as a separate species. The triploid associated with *A. jeffersonianum* was designated as *A. platineum* and that with *A. laterale* as *A. tremblayi*.

Positive field identification was impossible but laboratory examination of fresh tissue allowed chromosomes to be counted to identify diploids and triploids. Also, it was found that triploids had larger red blood cells, and some measurements of whole specimens would distinguish many individuals. However, the validity of naming the triploid forms as "species" has been questioned. In other groups of organisms hybrids do not retain a scientific name of their own but are referred to by a combined name derived from the potential names, i.e. *Ambystoma jeffersonianum* × *laterale*. Because the contribution of parental forms is unequal, in this case it has been suggested that *A. platineum* be referred to as *A. 2 jeffersonianum-laterale*, and *A. tremblayi* as *A. jeffersonianum-2 laterale*, to show clearly the relative contribution of the original hybridization.

More recent studies have even questioned the distinctiveness of separate triploid forms. The new work involves further use of an analysis technique termed *electrophonesis*, in which fresh tissue samples are placed on a jellied medium and subjected to electric current causing individual proteins to migrate through the jell at different speeds.

This allows precise comparison of the proteins between individuals. As the diploid species *(A. laterale* and *A. jeffersonianum)* differ in some of their proteins, their relative contributions to the hybrids can be compared. This technique originally confirmed the hybrid origin of the triploids but is currently being extended to extensive comparison of triploids from different populations. It also allows a search to be made for diploid hybrids whose presence would reinforce the conclusion that the triploids are not a ''species.''

In addition, the Blue-spotted Salamander is involved as part of another hybridizing pair of species. It interbreeds with the Smallmouth Salamander *(Ambystoma texanum)* on Lake Erie islands in Ohio, to produce both diploid and triploid hybrids. On North Bass Island, hybrids occur but both parental species are now apparently absent. Both *A. laterale* and *A. texanum* have been recorded on the Canadian Pelee Island in the same Lake Erie chain. Recently hybrids have also been identified, and populations on this island are being re-evaluated to determine the relative number of hybrids and parent forms.

For most purposes of a field biologist, individual specimens are best designated as the species in the complex they most closely resemble, with the realization that some hybrid individuals resembling one species or another may be included in such designations. For positive identification of a possible hybrid, the live individual should be taken to a specialist who has the laboratory facilities to examine chromosome numbers and protein content.

Blue-spotted Salamander
Salamandre à points bleus
Ambystoma laterale

The most brightly coloured member of the group, this salamander is also the smallest, reaching only 130 mm in length. It is black to bluish black above with a dark underside, and often has intense white or bluish flecking covering both the sides and underside. It occurs in much of Ontario, Quebec, New Brunswick and Prince Edward Island with only scattered occurrence in Nova Scotia, and ranges west to eastern Manitoba.

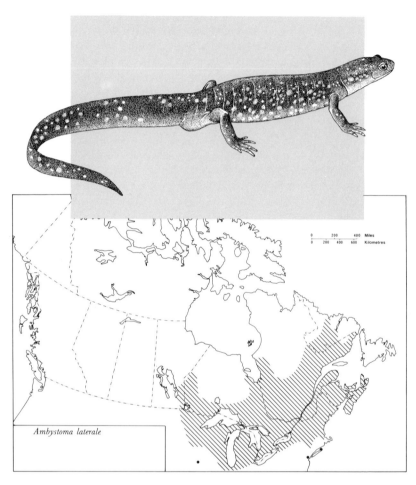

Ambystoma laterale

          The triploid associated with this species is usually longer and less spotted (any individual in an *A. laterale* population larger than 74 mm in snout to vent length is probably a triploid; smaller individuals may be either diploids or triploids). The triploid has been positively identified in Ontario, Quebec, New Brunswick and Nova Scotia along the southern border of the Blue-spotted Salamander range. In eastern Manitoba, northern Ontario and Quebec, Prince Edward Island, and most of New Brunswick and Nova Scotia only the diploid occurs.

Jefferson Salamander
Salamandre de Jefferson
Ambystoma jeffersonianum

In this larger, duller coloured form, the ground colour is brown to grey, and the underside is distinctly paler than the sides. The bluish spots are small, generally confined to limbs and lower sides. It has been recorded only in southwestern Ontario where it reaches the northern limit of a range extending much farther south in the United States than that of *A. laterale*. It reaches a maximum length of 210 mm.

The triploid form associated with it is usually somewhat smaller, and has more flecking. In Canada it has been found in most localities where the diploid is reported.

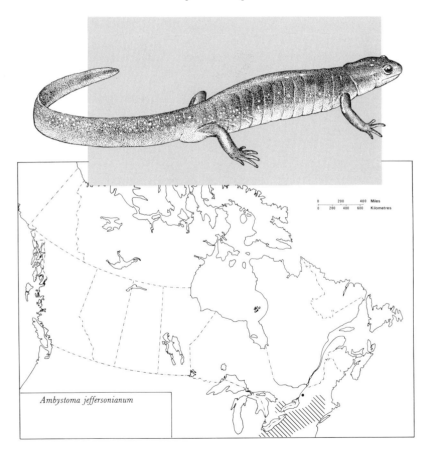

Ambystoma jeffersonianum

Smallmouth Salamander
Salamandre à nez court
Ambystoma texanum

A medium-sized salamander rarely exceeding about 140 mm, the Smallmouth Salamander is dark, either black or very dark brown, with profuse marking of lichen-like light grey over the sides, which may be reduced in some individuals. The head and mouth are relatively short and small compared to other species of *Ambystoma*. The toes are much shorter than the forms in the Jefferson Salamander complex. The Smallmouth Salamander has been recorded in Canada from Pelee Island, but hybrids may also occur on the mainland in southwestern Ontario.

Ambystoma texanum

Long-toed Salamander
Salamandre à longs doigts
Ambystoma macrodactylum

In form and size this species resembles the eastern *Ambystoma laterale*, with dark, generally black sides that may have many minute light flecks. However, it is boldly marked by a yellow or tan band on the back from snout to tail. In some areas this coloration may be variously broken into disconnected irregular patches down the back. It attains a maximum length of 175 mm.

Three subspecies have been recognized in Canada: the Northern Long-toed Salamander, *Ambystoma macrodactylum krausii*, generally has a continuous even-edged stripe and occurs in western Alberta and eastern British Columbia; the Eastern Long-toed Salamander, *A. m. columbianum*, usually has an uninterrupted stripe on the body but large distinct spots on the head and occurs in central British Columbia; the Western Long-toed Salamander, *A. m. macrodactylum*, has a dull stripe

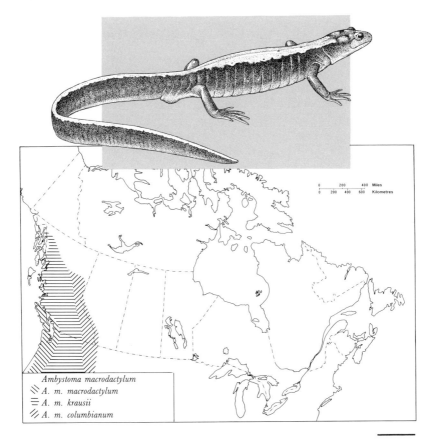

| 0 | 200 | 400 Miles |
| 0 | 200 | 400 | 600 Kilometres |

Ambystoma macrodactylum
\\\ *A. m. macrodactylum*
≡ *A. m. krausii*
//, *A. m. columbianum*

on the body, and the pigment on the head, snout and eyelids is broken
into diffuse flecks. It is recorded from southwestern mainland British
Columbia and Vancouver Island. The individual variation is great within
each of these forms, and identifications to subspecies can be made only
on the average coloration for a population. Further study is needed to define
correctly the boundaries and areas of interbreeding between subspecies
in British Columbia.

Yellow-spotted Salamander
Salamandre maculée
Ambystoma maculatum

    This moderately large salamander is black
above, pale grey beneath with a row of bright yellow or orange spots from
snout to tail on each side of the body. It reaches a length of 248 mm. The
species ranges widely over eastern Canada from Ontario to Prince Edward
Island.

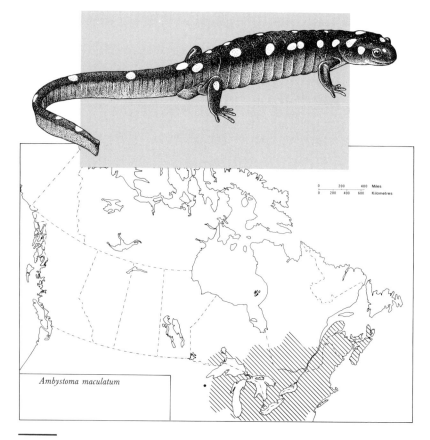

Ambystoma maculatum

Tiger Salamander
Salamandre tigrée
Ambystoma tigrinum

The largest species of the genus found in Canada, the Tiger Salamander is most variable in colour and pattern. It may be black or brown with yellow, cream or whitish spots, bars or reticulations above or with dark spots or bars on a brown or grey background,

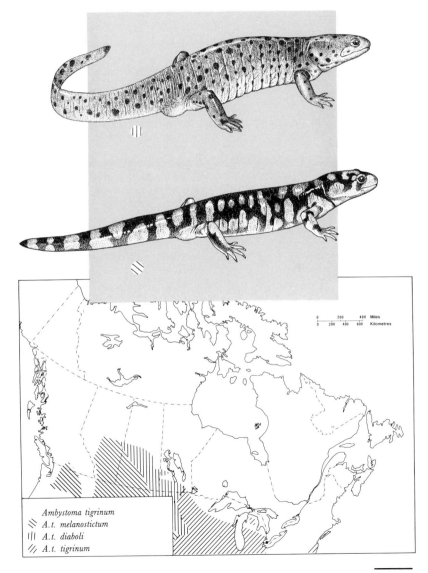

Ambystoma tigrinum
\\\ *A.t. melanostictum*
||| *A.t. diaboli*
// *A.t. tigrinum*

depending on the subspecies. Large larvae may be neotenic (assuming an adult coloration and becoming sexually mature while retaining their gills). This phenomenon sometimes occurs in drier areas such as the southern portions of the Prairie Provinces. Three subspecies are currently recognized in Canada, but the variation within the central and western portion of the country is poorly understood and probably will result in revisions of the current arrangement. The record length reported is 330 mm but about 203 mm is a good-sized individual.

The subspecies Eastern Tiger Salamander, *A. t. tigrinum*, is typically black with yellow to dull olive spots scattered over the back and sides; some old individuals may be olive with brown to black spots and reticulations. The belly is olive-yellow, marked with darker pigment. This form has been recorded only in southern Ontario from Point Pelee and Pelee Island. Populations just east of the Red River in Manitoba approach it in coloration and may indicate a zone of intergradation between this and the following subspecies.

The Grey Tiger Salamander, *A. t. diaboli*, is typically light olive to brown or almost black, with dark brown to black spots, and irregular bars or reticulations. It ranges through southern Manitoba at least to central Saskatchewan but the extent of the zone of transition with the Blotched Tiger Salamander is poorly known.

The Blotched Tiger Salamander, *A. t. melanostictum*, has a highly irregular pattern, comprising whitish, yellow or olive spots, with blotches or reticulations whose borders often merge with the ground colour of brown or black, sometimes darkest bordering the diffuse light markings. This form occurs in southern Saskatchewan and Alberta and in the more arid southern valleys of British Columbia. Together, the races *A. t. diaboli* and *A. t. melanostictum* occupy the short-grass prairie and Aspen Parkland zones—from eastern Manitoba to the foothills of the Rockies—but do not penetrate north into the coniferous Boreal Forest. Over this portion of their range they are the only salamander species that occur.

Northwestern Salamander
Salamandre foncée
Ambystoma gracile

This moderately large, brown salamander is blackish above and lighter below, with a maximum length of about 200 mm. It is the only Canadian salamander with parotoid glands (large oval glands on the back over the front legs). These may be lighter brown than the general ground colour. At high altitudes it is known to be neotenic, but the extent of the occurrence of this in Canadian populations is unknown.

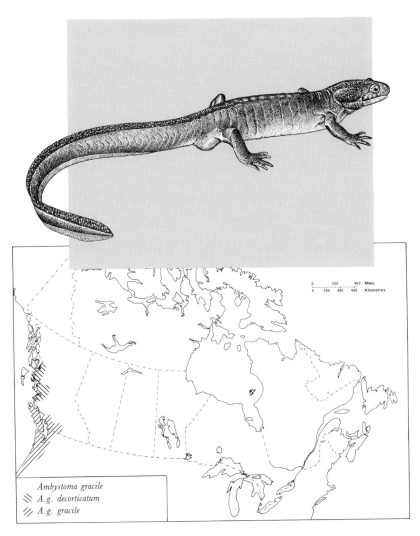

Ambystoma gracile
\\\ A.g. decorticatum
/// A.g. gracile

Two races occur in Canada: the Brown Salamander, *A. g. gracile*, in southwestern coastal British Columbia and Vancouver Island is uniformly dark, blackish brown above and lighter below, with 10 or 11 costal grooves. The British Columbia Salamander, *A. g. decorticatum*, occurs in coastal British Columbia north to coastal Alaska. It is marked with irregular whitish, yellowish or bronze spots and dots on the back, with 11 or 12 costal grooves. The number of vertebrae, and therefore the variation in costal grooves, has been shown experimentally to vary with the temperature at which the eggs develop: on the average lower temperatures produce young with more vertebrae.

Pacific Giant Salamander
Grande Salamandre
Dicamptodon ensatus

This massive ambystomatid salamander, which can attain a length of 305 mm, is placed in a separate genus that includes only two species; only *D. ensatus* reaches into extreme southwestern British Columbia. It has brown to purplish ground colour boldly marked with black. It frequents the vicinity of cold streams, seepages and the margins of mountain lakes, usually in deep forest habitat. The eggs are laid in streams and often hidden under stones in shallow water. It has been recorded from only two areas in British Columbia, the Cultus and

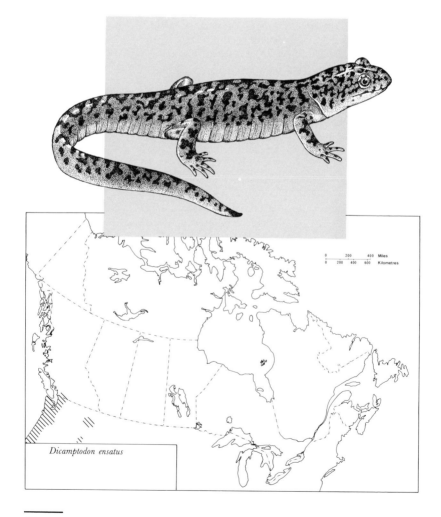

Dicamptodon ensatus

42

Chilliwack lakes drainages. It may be active both in the day and the night and has been reported to climb trees and bushes up to 2.4 m above ground. The larvae differ from the pond-type larvae of *Ambystoma* with shorter gills and lower dorsal and ventral tail fins to adapt them to their stream environment.

Family Plethodontidae
Lungless Salamanders

The family Plethodontidae is the largest group of salamanders in the world containing 214 species (64% of known salamanders) and 23 genera (44%). The centre of its abundance and diversity is the southeastern United States but it is also numerous on the west coast of North America and through Central and South America. It is the only salamander family to occur in the tropics. Two species representing a single genus in Europe are the only occurrences outside the Americas. Seven genera and eight species are native to Canada; an additional genus and species recorded were probably introduced.

All salamanders in this family lack lungs. They inhabit moist environments, streams, spring and river margins, and damp woodlands but they are often arboreal in the tropics. Generally, they are small, relatively slender, with prominent costal grooves and upward protruding eyes. A distinct small groove runs from the nostril to the upper lip on each side. Although this groove may be difficult to detect in small individuals without using a magnifying glass, its presence immediately identifies the salamander to family, and distinguishes it from some of the smaller woodland *Ambystoma*, which may be superficially similar in shape and colour pattern.

In life history patterns the family is variable. The stream-dwelling representatives *(Eurycea, Gyrinophilus)* lay eggs in the water and have depressed, streamlined stream-type larvae with relatively small gills and reduced tail fins. These may spend at least one winter as larvae before transforming. Most woodland forms *(Plethodon, Ensatina, Aneides)* lay their eggs on land, in rotting logs, or similar moist habitats, and have a supressed larval development in which the young complete the gilled larval stage within the eggs, hatching as miniatures of the adults. Hatching occurs during the same summer the eggs are laid. Often the female remains with the eggs, perhaps to guard them or to protect them from drying out in dry periods. The Four-toed Salamander, *Hemidactylium scutatum*, lays its eggs on land, in damp sphagnum moss over bog pools, and the young hatch as larvae and drop to the pool below to complete their development in the water. The Dusky Salamander, *Desmognathus fuscus*, also lays its eggs on land, in sphagnum or under logs or stones near the water. The larvae may stay a short period at the moist hatching site before moving to the water to complete their development.

During dry periods, particularly in midsummer, both stream and woodland species may retreat beneath the surface of the ground. But in spring and fall, and in periods of soaking rains, they will be found near the surface, under stones, logs and similar cover during the day, and often wandering in the open at night. They feed on a wide variety of insects and other invertebrate animals.

Being lungless, these salamanders depend on moist skin and the roof of the mouth for respiration (obtaining oxygen from, and expelling carbon dioxide to, the air). Since a moist surface is essential for this exchange, they are highly intolerant of dryness and soon die if exposed to a drying environment. They are also intolerant of excessive heat. Stream forms do not invade stagnant, warm, poorly oxygenated waters, and woodland forms are not found in prairie and parkland habitats.

Dusky Salamander
Salamandre sombre
Desmognathus fuscus

The coloration of the Dusky Salamander is variable but generally is grey or brown with muddy markings that may stand out well from the ground colour, particularly in smaller individuals, or be only slightly distinguishable from it in larger, older specimens. In juveniles, there are five to eight pairs of round spots down the back, which are bordered by a wavy dark line. This pattern becomes more obscure with age but the dark usually remains as spots or dashes. A light line from the eye back to the angle of the jaw is usually present. The general shape is often sufficient to tell a Dusky from other salamanders in the family in Canada. Its hind legs are markedly larger and sturdier than the front (in fact, if escaping it often jumps away with a thrust and a wiggle and can be exceedingly difficult to hold even for a brief, close look). The area behind the head has a somewhat swollen appearance, and the lower jaw is stiff. This salamander opens its mouth by moving the upper jaw up, rather than the lower jaw down. There is a pronounced sharp ridge along the upper side of the tail. It attains a maximum length of 141 mm.

The Dusky Salamander occurs in southern Quebec and southern New Brunswick, usually in or along edges of streams, springs and their seepage areas. An old record "opposite Buffalo" in southern Ontario may be from a now extinct population, though further searching in the Niagara Gorge area might yet reveal them.

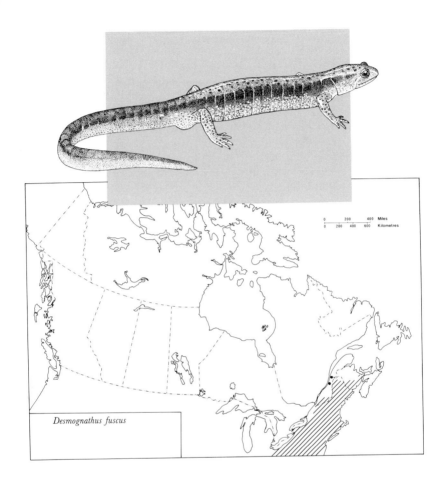

Desmognathus fuscus

Two-lined Salamander
Salamandre à deux lignes
Eurycea bislineata

Yellowish brown on the back and yellow on the underside, this salamander gets its name from the pair of longitudinal dark lines down the back, prominent on young specimens, but more obscure on larger, darker individuals. There is usually a peppering of small dark spots down the back in the light area defined by the dark lines, and some dark spotting or mottling on the sides. The hind legs are only slightly larger than the front, not conspicuously bigger as in the Dusky Salamander. It attains a maximum size of 121 mm.

The Two-lined Salamander occurs through central and eastern Ontario, (but is absent from southwestern and northern Ontario), a major portion of Quebec and reaches southwestern Labrador.

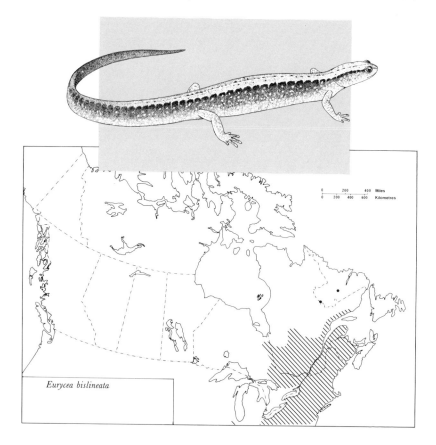

Eurycea bislineata

It is widespread in New Brunswick but absent from Nova Scotia. It is an inhabitant of streams, small rivers, and occasionally, rocky lake edges, although it may wander some distance into adjoining woodland during summer wet periods.

Spring Salamander
Salamandre pourpre
Gyrinophilus porphyriticus

The Spring Salamander is the largest of the stream salamanders found in Canada, and one of the largest representatives of its family, with a record length of 219 mm. The general coloration is a pinkish or yellowish brown with vague darker markings, which give it a clouded appearance. Generally, there is a light line from eye to nostril with a grey border below it, but this varies from fairly prominent to barely noticeable.

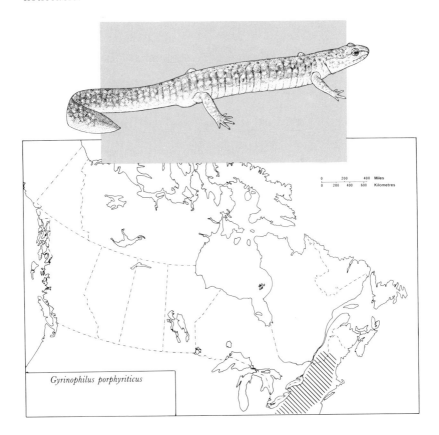

Gyrinophilus porphyriticus

This species occurs in and along streams in extreme southern Quebec. A locality that yielded larvae in 1877 "opposite Buffalo" in southwestern Ontario has never been rediscovered, and no other valid Ontario records are known.

Four-toed Salamander
Salamandre à quatre doigts
Hemidactylium scutatum

This small salamander, generally less than 102 mm long, is easily recognized. Although its reddish to greyish brown back is rather nondescript, it has a distinctive glossy white belly with prominent black dots over it. The hind feet have four toes rather than five as in all other salamanders found in Canada, except the Mudpuppy which

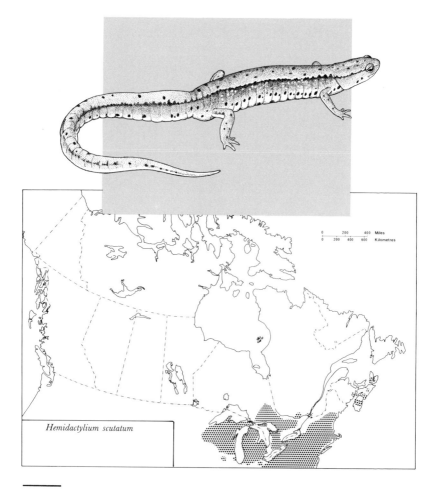

Hemidactylium scutatum

is much larger and has external gills. A prominent constriction at the base of the tail is a convenient break-point if a predator grabs the salamander from behind. Most lungless salamanders will shed their tails readily if they are struggling to escape but this one accomplishes the feat with particular ease.

Its distribution is apparently most nearly continuous through southern Ontario and western Quebec, with what seems to be isolated relict populations in southern Quebec. It is quite widespread in Nova Scotia, but was unrecorded from New Brunswick until 1983, and this may mainly reflect lack of intensive searching for this species there. The Four-toed Salamander is characteristically an inhabitant of sphagnum bogs and lays its eggs in moss over bog pools. It will also wander in woodland and in damp weather even cross areas that are usually dry.

Larvae representative of major families of salamanders in Canada. Top: Salamandridae *(Notophthalmus viridescens)*; middle: Plethodontidae *(Eurycea bislineata)*; bottom: Ambystomatidae *(Ambystoma tigrinum)*.

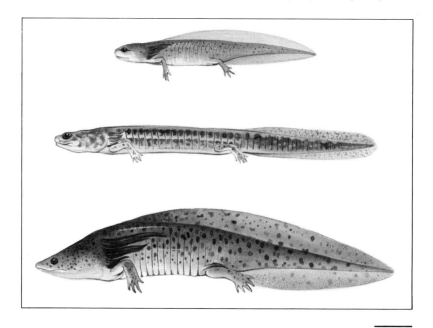

Eastern Redback Salamander
Salamandre rayée
Plethodon cinereus

This salamander is abundant in eastern Canada wherever white pine, northern hemlock or deciduous woodland remain. It is usually less than 102 mm long and shows three main colour variations. The red-backed has a broad stripe down the back from snout to tail, which is normally red, but may be reddish brown or yellowish in some populations. It has dull black, grey or lead-coloured sides. The lead-backed variation has this colour uniformly over the sides and back. The third form, termed *erythristic*, which is the rarest variant of the three, is entirely red over sides and back, though it may show varying amounts of dull brownish mottling. The underside of all three is mottled dark and white in about

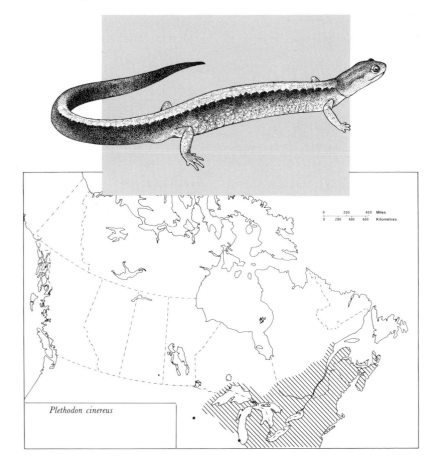

Plethodon cinereus

equal quantities. Red- and lead-backed phases occur over all the Canadian range but vary greatly in relative numbers; some populations may be composed entirely of red-backs, a few entirely of lead-backs. The reasons for this variation in proportions are not clear. It occurs from Prince Edward Island to northwestern Ontario and is most often found under logs and stones in damp woodland, particularly in spring and fall.

Western Redback Salamander
Salamandre à dos rayé
Plethodon vehiculum

The striped phase is the most prevalent form of this western woodland salamander but its colour is variable—reddish, orange, tan or yellow. The dorsal stripe may occasionally be almost completely obscured by dark pigment. The sides are dark, the belly mottled

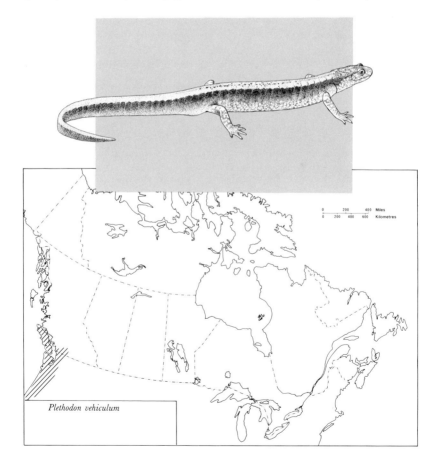

Plethodon vehiculum

with dark and light, and it is usually less than 127 mm long. It has fewer costal grooves than the eastern species, generally 16 in comparison to 19 for northern *P. cinereus* (when the grooves are counted to include the one over the front leg and the one at the anterior edge of the hind leg, with both forks of any forked grooves counted in this region). In Canada, it is restricted to the moist forests of southwestern mainland British Columbia and Vancouver Island, where it is found under bark, rotting wood and leaves. Like the Eastern Redback Salamander, it lays large yolked eggs in hollows in rotting logs. The young pass the gilled larval stage within the egg.

Eschscholtz's Salamander
Salamandre variable
Ensatina eschscholtzi

Canadian representatives of this species are uniformly coloured, yellowish to reddish brown with very fine black speckling above and pale grey or whitish underparts, which appear somewhat transparent. Eschscholtz's Salamander reaches a total length of 114 mm. There are 12 to 13 grooves, and the tail has a swollen appearance with a marked constriction at its base. Eschscholtz's Salamander occurs in moist forest in extreme southwest mainland British Columbia and southern Vancouver Island. The only subspecies found in Canada is *Ensatina eschscholtzi oregonensis*, but six other races occur in southern California. These include colour variations that are black with yellow or orange blotches, and varigated patterns combine these colours. Although most subspecies intergrade with each other, generally in fairly wide contact zones, the southern range is split by the central arid valley of California. Where the eastern and western forms contact in the north, intergraded populations are found, but where they meet in the south, they fail to interbreed, and maintain their distinctiveness. This type of circular distribution of populations around some uninhabitable region where interbreeding occurs everywhere except at one point of overlap is most interesting to students of evolution. At the southern overlap they behave like two distinct species, but elsewhere like subspecies. The distribution and variations of *Ensatina* are some of the most thoroughly studied examples of this phenomenon.

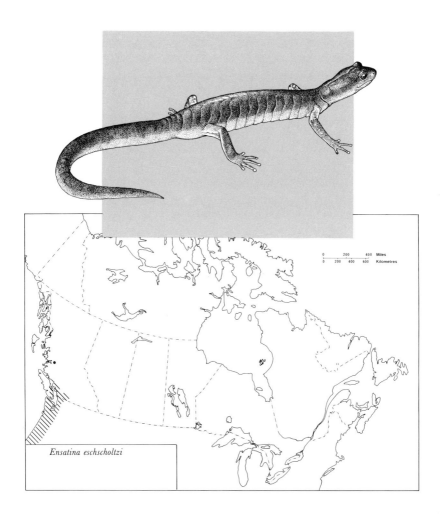

Ensatina eschscholtzi

Clouded Salamander
Salamandre pommelée
Aneides ferreus

Reaching a maximum length of 127 mm, this slender, long-legged salamander is black to brown, with vague ashy yellowish-grey mottlings over the back and sides, giving it its common name. It may occasionally be speckled with bronze and a few whitish spots. The underside is metallic grey, it usually has 16 costal grooves, and its distinctive toe tips are squarish. In Canada it has only been recorded on Vancouver Island and some small adjacent islands but where it occurs it is widespread and locally abundant. It is commonly found under bark of trees or logs, but will wander overland on rainy nights. It climbs readily and has been found as high as 6 m up in trees.

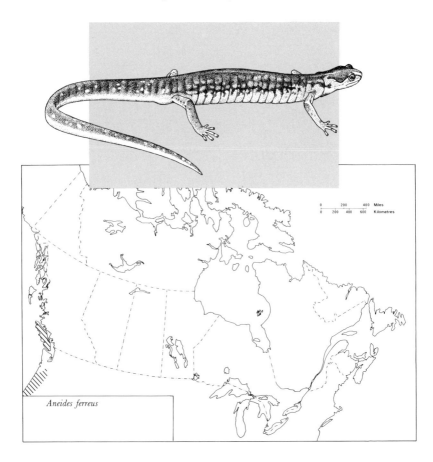

Aneides ferreus

Red Salamander
Salamandre rousse
Pseudotriton ruber

The maximum length of this salamander is 181 mm. It is red or orange coloured and heavily marked on the underside with black spots. The absence of a light and a dark line from eye to nostril distinguishes it from the Spring Salamander.

It occurs in and along field and woodland streams that have sandy, rocky or gravelly bottoms. There is only one known Canadian specimen, which was collected in 1946 at Dunchurch in the Parry Sound District of Ontario, and the nearest United States records are 322 km south in southern New York State and northern Pennsylvania. This salamander is often a favourite item with bait fisherman in its United States range, and the single Canadian record may represent an inadvertent introduction by fishing tourists. Repeated searches of the area in recent years have failed to find it again.

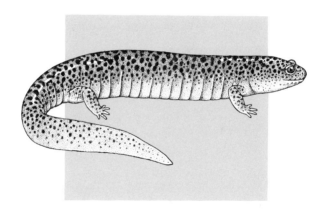

Order Anura
Frogs, Toads and Treefrogs

The Anura, the tail-less amphibians, are very distinctive vertebrates characterized by squat, compact bodies, disproportionately large heads and long, muscular, hind legs. Although English has only two words to designate the primary groups of anurans—frogs and toads—there are actually 24 distinctive families. The compounds formed to designate them (eg. treefrogs, tailed frogs, spadefoot toads) do not necessarily indicate any true relationship among families. It is perhaps best to use frogs as the inclusive term for the whole group. Toads, strictly applied, are the very warty, terrestrial frogs in the genus *Bufo*.

Frogs comprise 85% of living species in the class Amphibia, with 2770 recognized species throughout the world. In contrast to the salamanders, which are primarily a North Temperate group (except for the successful radiation of the family Plethodontidae into the New World tropics), frogs are widespread and successful on all continents except Antarctica. The order is dominated by five families which together contain 77% of frog species: Bufonidae (toads), 279; Hylidae (treefrogs), 395; Ranidae (true frogs), 556; Leptodactylidae (southern frogs), 650; and Microhylidae (narrow-mouthed frogs), 232. Of these dominant families only the Bufonidae, Hylidae and Ranidae occur throughout Canada south of the tundra. Two other families are represented, but are more restricted: the Pelobatidae (spadefoot toads) occur in arid portions of the central and western region of Canada, and the Ascaphidae are found in mountain streams of the western region.

Frogs have successfully radiated into a variety of habitats—terrestrial, aquatic and arboreal, with little modification of their basic build. Some have highly toxic skin secretions, but most depend on sudden leaps or camouflaging coloration to avoid predators. All frogs show similar feeding habits, with some variation imposed by different sizes and habitats. All feed primarily on invertebrates, particularly insects, but large individuals occasionally eat small birds, mammals, reptiles and other frogs, even smaller members of their own species.

All Canadian frogs lay their eggs in water, but in tropical regions of the world there has been a radiation of forms that lay eggs in moist places on land, particularly among the very successful Leptodactylidae. The eggs of Canadian species hatch into tadpoles, rotund bodied, initially legless, larvae with muscular tails, which usually have broad median fins above and below. Tadpoles obtain oxygen through gills, which are external at hatching but internal soon after, becoming covered by the growth of a fold of skin, the operculum, behind the cheek region. An external outlet for water, the spiracle, remains within the opening and is usually located on the left side of the head.

Tadpoles soon develop hind limb buds, which grow into legs by the time the tadpoles transform into frogs. The front legs, however, develop within the gill chambers, and are not visible until they push through the skin, fully formed, just before transformation. Other tadpole characteristics include a small mouth with rasping teeth, and a long coiled intestine. These change to the enlarged mouth and short intestine of frogs at transformation when the tail is resorbed as well. This period marks a major feeding change from the largely vegetarian or small animal diet of tadpoles to the larger, active, animal prey of frogs. Also characteristic of frogs is a well-developed tongue attached at the front of the mouth, which is flipped out to catch small prey such as insects.

The males of most frog species have mating calls during the breeding season; each species has a clearly distinctive call from that of the other species in the same region. In Canada, only some populations of the Western Toad, *Bufo boreas*, and the Tailed Frog, *Ascaphus truei*, lack mating calls. In most Canadian species, males congregate in large numbers in ponds or lakes during the breeding season, and the simultaneous vocalizations of many individuals together often produce a deafening chorus during the peak of breeding. Females tend to spend a shorter period at the breeding area, mating soon after arriving and leaving soon after laying their eggs. Males, which may mate with several females in one season, resume calling after mating. Generally, the breeding call serves to attract the female, and perhaps additional males, to the breeding site, and to guide the female to a male of her own species when several species are breeding simultaneously in the same area. However, a few species are territorial and will actively defend a chosen calling site. In these circumstances the call functions to warn other males away from a given site.

Other vocalizations include a "protest chirp," which a male gives if embraced by another male, presumably a signal that he is not a female. Some species also give alarm calls when frightened and a loud terror call when grabbed by a predator, such as a garter snake, from which there is little chance of escape.

Family Ascaphidae
Tailed Frogs

The most primitive frogs in the world live in the western portion of North America and in New Zealand. Some herpetologists regard these as representing two separate ancient families of ancestral frogs, while others unite them under a single family. The single species of *Ascaphus* occurs in the mountains from British Columbia to California and is restricted to cold, swift-flowing streams. The tadpole has a sucker-like mouth disc ideally suited for clinging to submerged rocks to avoid being swept downstream. *Leiopelma*, the other primitive genus, is represented by three species, which are the only frogs native to New Zealand. These lack the tadpole stage, development being completed in the egg, although the little frogs still have tails at hatching. The eggs are laid in moist places on land.

These frogs, though they lack true tails as adults, retain tiny "tail-wagging" muscles as a vestige of their evolution from ancestors with tails. Their ribs are not fused to the backbone, as is the case in all other frogs.

Tailed Frog
Grenouille-à-queue
Ascaphus truei

This small frog, not exceeding 51 mm, often has a rough, somewhat warty skin and a rather flat-bodied appearance. Its colour is grey, olive or brown to reddish, clouded or speckled with black, with a dark line from snout to front leg, intercepted only by the eye, with shallow V-shaped marking between the eyes. The pupil of the eye is vertical in bright light. The parotoid glands are low and inconspicuous, but reach from behind the eye to the shoulder on each side. There is no eardrum (tympanum). Males have a tail-like organ for internal fertilization with a vent on its lower side near the tip. Breeding males also have small black pads on the palms of the front feet, on the arms and on the upper chest. The female has no tail or dark pads.

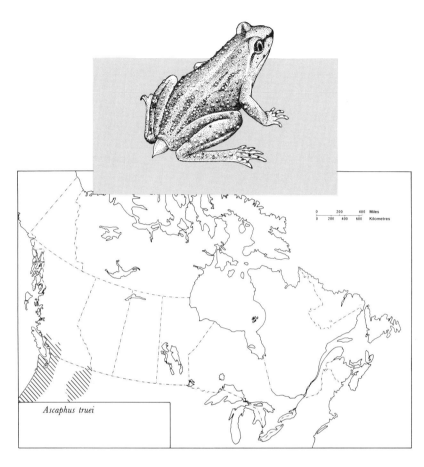

Ascaphus truei

Ascaphus is found in the southwestern mainland along the lower coast of British Columbia but not on Vancouver Island and has been recorded once from extreme southeastern British Columbia. Since it requires clear, cold, rocky streams in humid forests, extensive lumbering may pose a threat to its survival in some localities. The eggs are laid in strings under rocks, and the adults are active along stream margins, particularly at night, but also may hunt in the adjacent damp woods.

Family Pelobatidae
Spadefoot Toads

The spadefoots are a small family containing 64 species, all quite distinct from true toads. They are squat, compact, short-legged anurans, with delicate appearing, somewhat warty, skins. However, they lack the parotoid glands that are a prominent feature of Canadian true toads *(Bufo)*. There are two subfamilies: Megophryinae of southeastern Asia includes six genera; Pelobatinae consists of *Pelobates* of Europe and northern Africa and *Scaphiopus* of North America.

Two species of *Scaphiopus* are found in the arid areas of the central and western regions of Canada. Adults of both can achieve a maximum length of 38 to 51 mm. They have vertical eye pupils in bright light as does the Tailed Frog, *Ascaphus*, the only other Canadian anuran to have this type of pupil. All our other toads, frogs and treefrogs have round or horizontal pupils (even the pupils of *Scaphiopus* and *Ascaphus* appear round when fully open in the dark). There is a black horny projection on the under edge of each hind foot, the ''spade,'' which is used in burrowing into loose soil, backwards, as true toads do. True toads have two tubercles on each hind foot, though one is much larger than the other.

Spadefoots breed after heavy rains in late spring or early summer, and huge choruses form suddenly at such times in ditches, sloughs and flooded fields. The call is short and bleating and carries a long distance. The eggs are laid in irregular cylindrical clusters, and hatching and development of the tadpoles to transformation are exceptionally rapid, taking as little as two to three weeks. This is of prime importance in arid regions where the breeding sites dry up quickly. The light-coloured spadefoot tadpoles are chunky in body outline, largest behind the eyes. Papillae encircle the entire mouth with a small gap occasionally present in the middle of them. There are usually four or five rows of teeth above the mouth and four or five below. The eyes are very close together on the top of the head. Although spadefoot tadpoles feed mainly on algae, some may become carnivorous, and even cannibalistic, especially in the Plains Spadefoot.

Except when breeding, adults forage for insects, particularly on rainy nights, and may spend prolonged dry periods inactive, burrowed under the ground.

Plains Spadefoot
Crapaud des Plaines
Scaphiopus bombifrons

This species has a pronounced solid raised boss, underlain with bone, between the eyes. The general coloration is usually pale, dusky brown, greyish or greenish, sometimes with four light stripes, the pair on the back in an hourglass configuration. The small warts may be tipped with yellow or orange. The Plains Spadefoot occurs most abundantly in the short-grass prairie of southeastern Alberta and southwestern Saskatchewan. There are scattered records from eastern Saskatchewan and southwestern Manitoba. A record from just north of Riding Mountain National Park in the prairie-like region near Dauphin may represent an isolated population.

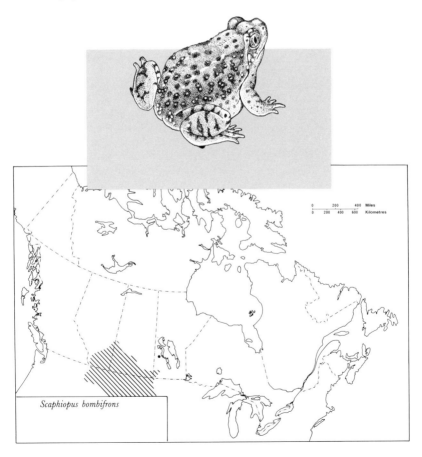

Scaphiopus bombifrons

Great Basin Spadefoot
Crapaud du Grand Bassin
Scaphiopus intermontanus

This species is similar to the Plains Spadefoot but somewhat darker in coloration. The hourglass marking and ash-grey lateral streaks are more often prominent. The boss between the eyes is less prominent and is glandular, rather than bony.

The Great Basin Spadefoot occupies the arid valleys of south-central British Columbia in a habitat similar to that of its relative in the Great Plains.

Scaphiopus intermontanus

Family Bufonidae
Toads

The true toads (Bufonidae) are found throughout the world, except in Australia, Antarctica and Greenland among the major land masses. One species, the Giant Toad, *Bufo marinus*, has recently been introduced into Australia, and other introductions have occurred in those West Indian islands that originally lacked toads, in Hawaii and New Guinea.

The family contains 20 genera and 279 species, which include a diversity of forms from the bony and brightly coloured *Atelopus* of Central and South America, to the *Nectophrynoides* of Africa, one of the few live-bearing anurans. Reproductive habits are also diverse: one genus, *Ansomia*, the Philippine toads, breeds in mountain torrents and has a tadpole with a sucker-like mouth for clinging to rocks; other genera lay eggs on land that hatch directly into tiny toadlets. The majority of species, however, including all Canadian kinds, lay eggs in shallow quiet water and have a tadpole stage.

The most widespread and familiar genus in this family is *Bufo*—the "typical" toads: squat, short-legged anurans, generally thick-skinned and rough appearing, covered with warts, and usually with very large, prominent, oval or kidney-shaped parotoid glands over the shoulders. Usually there are prominent bony ridges, cranial and postorbital crests, between and behind the eyes. Toads are well equipped for a largely terrestrial life; their compact shape, short limbs and thick skin help to reduce water loss in dry periods. A large urinary bladder can act as a water storage organ during dry periods. Their hind feet have a pair of conified projections—metatarsal tubercles—the outer larger than the inner. These look and function like the spades of spadefoots for digging into the earth, which a toad does backwards, hind feet first, using a shuffling motion that allows it to literally sink into the ground. It may remain with only the top of its head exposed for temporary concealment, or it may continue to dig until it is some distance under the surface, the soil above it falling in to cover it over and conceal where it has taken refuge.

There are 194 species of *Bufo* throughout the world. Canadian species are entirely terrestrial except for a period in spring, or after heavy rains, where they congregate to breed in temporary ponds, ditches, shallow edges of lakes or backwaters or other quiet areas in rivers and streams. Usually they are most vocal on warm, humid nights, but often they can be heard in the daytime. Typically, *Bufo* lay eggs in two long, simultaneously produced strings, one from each oviduct.

Toad tadpoles are characteristically black above and below, though they tend to lighten to a grey or brown as transformation approaches and the pattern of warts becomes evident. They have horny beaks and usually two rows of teeth on the upper lip and three on the lower. The mouth papillae are at the sides only, and the sides of the mouth are indented. The eyes are close together on the top of the head. The closeness of the eyes of toad tadpoles, which contrasts to the pop-eyed look of the tadpoles of treefrogs, and the dark underside identify them.

Since tadpole development depends on temperature, they transform into tiny toads anytime from late June to July or early August depending on the latitude, how warm the summer has been and the depth of the pond. The tiny toadlets give no clue to the size of the adults: Canadian species are comparatively minute at transformation, less than 10 mm total length. Adult toads are generally 45 to 127 mm in Canadian species. As soon as the toadlet leaves the pond from which it transformed, growth is so rapid that it may have more than doubled or even tripled its size by fall. It hibernates for the winter, and rapid growth begins again the next year to assure breeding size by the following spring. In warmer areas to the south, where there is shorter or no enforced winter hibernation at all, toads may complete development to breeding size by the season following transformation.

There is a tremendous spread in the size of young toads because the egg-laying season may span a month or more and transformation several weeks. Often enormous numbers of young toads transform at a breeding site, and a windrow of toadlets may cover the margins of a pond. Some species tend to disperse during rains, hence the occasional observation of "rains of toads" in a particularly successful reproductive year. The mortality rate of young toads is very high and few survive to their first breeding season. Even among adults, fewer than a third of the males present in one breeding season may return to that site the following year, and the percentage drops more rapidly in subsequent years. However, individual toads have been known to survive in the wild for at least eight years.

After breeding size is reached, further growth in adult toads is slight from year to year. The time of transformation and their growth rate when young are the major factors in different sizes of adults. The growth rate is dependent on a wide range of variables, primarily the amount of time they have for feeding and digestion and probably the amount of energy they have to spend hunting to fill their stomachs. These variables depend on temperature and relative moisture—damp, warm periods are best for toad activity—and the abundance of insects and other invertebrates for food. Since moisture, temperature and abundance of prey may vary greatly over short distances, differences in growth could be noticeable within a small area.

Outside their breeding season, toads are generally solitary, and may move some distance from the breeding area. People have often observed a toad establish a summer residence in some favourable place, under a step, or in the shelter of a bush, and remain there all one season, coming out to feed at regular intervals, usually late in the day. A resident toad may appear in the same place year after year, but it is uncertain whether this represents the same individual or a particularly suitable place frequented by different individuals in successive years.

Toads are voracious feeders, taking whatever invertebrate prey is most abundant at the time, tackling larger and larger prey as they themselves grow. There is even a recorded case of an adult toad unsuccessfully attempting to eat a baby Red-winged Blackbird, which had apparently fallen out of its nest and must have been fluttering on the water surface.

The feeding strategy of toads is like that of a great majority of frogs. They generally do not recognize prey unless it moves. They may stalk it methodically until they are within striking distance, then the fleshy tongue, attached at the front of the mouth, flips out suddenly, the sticky pronged tips touch the intended meal, and tongue and prey flip back into the mouth in one smooth instantaneous motion, which is so rapid the human eye hardly sees more than the opening and closing of the mouth. The eyes of a toad may be drawn downward to help push a large item into the throat. The front legs are used for particularly large prey and, in a rapid shuffle, stuff the protruding portions of an ungainly meal into the mouth. Toads, like frogs, generally eat their own skins when they shed, using the forelimbs to push the skin down the throat.

The warts and parotoid glands of toads produce a poison that is highly toxic to some animals. When a toad is roughly handled this exudes as a sticky white substance. It has been reported that very large toads, such as *Bufo marinus* of Texas, Central and South America, have poisoned dogs foolish enough to swallow them. Usually, however, a toad picked up in the mouth is enough to deter any dog, which soon releases it to paw its mouth and try to rid itself of the taste. Toad mucous transferred to the mouth from hands that have held toads, even in minute quantities, can produce a numbing sensation that lasts for some time. Some animals, such as snakes of the genera *Thamnophis* (garter snakes), *Nerodia* (water snakes) and *Heterodon* (Hognose Snakes) can eat toads without ill effect, swallowing them whole and digesting them poison and all. Some predatory birds and mammals have learned to eat the toad and leave the skin, thus avoiding the poison. However, despite the potency of the poison, it does not account for the long-standing myth that toads cause warts. Probably this misapprehension arose because toads themselves are warty in a day when the form of animals and plants was thought to contain a clue to their usefulness or harm to humans.

With their voracious appetites and their predilection for insects, toads are a welcome fixture in gardens, eating an impressive volume of insect pests for their size.

Five distinct varieties of toads representing four species occur in Canada. Three of these are widespread, replacing each other from east to west across the country and occurring from the southern border nearly to the limit of continuous forest. Two other species, both widespread in the United States, barely penetrate north of the Canadian border. All are quite similar in habits and life history, though prairie species are more dependent on heavy rains to stimulate breeding activity, while others simply respond to rising spring temperatures where the presence of water is more assured, though even they are more active during and immediately after warm rains. The most important characters for recognizing Canadian toads are the presence and structure of the bony cranial crests between the eyes, the number of warts in the dorsal spots and, in one case, the relation of the postorbital crests (the bony ridges behind the eyes) to the parotoid gland.

American Toad
Crapaud d'Amérique
Bufo americanus
Two very distinctive and widespread subspecies are now included under this species. They are distinguishable on the basis of structure, colour and geographic range, and were until recently regarded as separate species.

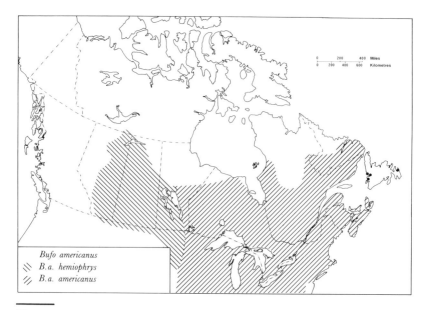

Bufo americanus
B.a. *hemiophrys*
B.a. *americanus*

American Toad
Bufo americanus americanus

The American Toad, *Bufo americanus americanus*, is an average-sized toad, usually 51 to 114 mm long with the largest size, as in all Canadian toads, being achieved by adult females. Colour is usually some shade of brown, but grey, red, green or yellow may predominate and occasionally, particularly in damp cool surroundings, they may be almost black. The warts may stand out as red or brown in contrast to a duller general body colour. The American Toad may be strongly patterned, with dark spots on the back and sides or streaks of light and dark on the sides. The underside is often heavily patterned with spots or reticulations but occasionally there will be few or no spots. The cranial crests are usually prominent and diverge at the back; the postorbital crests are well developed and often have backward spurs at their lateral edges that separate them from the anterior edges of the parotoid glands.

This is a toad of the deciduous and boreal forests of eastern North America. It ranges north to Ungava, James Bay, and possibly the coast of Hudson Bay, and from Prince Edward Island to eastern Manitoba. It has been introduced to parts of Newfoundland.

Northern populations have often been recognized as a distinct subspecies, the Hudson Bay Toad, *B. a. copei*, partly because of its vivid red or orange markings. However, the area of intermediates between these northern populations and the duller-coloured toads of southern Ontario and Quebec is so broad that use of a distinctive name for the former is not justified. At the junction of the Boreal Forest and Aspen Parkland in eastern Manitoba, the American Toad hybridizes in a narrow zone with the related subspecies, the Canadian Toad, to create individuals that have a mixture of the features of the two and can only be referred to as *Bufo americanus americanus* × *hemiophrys*.

Canadian Toad
Bufo americanus hemiophrys

This subspecies is generally slightly smaller than the related *B. a. americanus*, and tends to be more drab in colour—dull brown, grey, occasionally greenish, and rarely, rust-coloured. Generally there is less contrast between warts and ground colour. Usually it has prominent large spots with more and somewhat smaller warts than has *B. a. americanus*. The underside is typically less densely spotted. The most characteristic feature, however, is the cranial crests, which are often parallel, or diverge anteriorly, never posteriorly. The postorbital crests may be reduced or absent. The crests between the eyes are always bridged behind and usually filled in between to some extent. This may vary, from a groove between them to a solid filling-in, which unifies the crests to form a single solid boss between the eyes.

The Canadian Toad is abundant in the sloughs, potholes, river floodplains and lake margins of the Aspen Parkland of the central portion of Canada. It also ranges north in the central Boreal Forest at least to Fort Smith in the Northwest Territories and southwest into the grassland of southern Alberta and Saskatchewan. It does not penetrate far south of Canada as do most of our abundant species, but ranges only as far as northern South Dakota, except for an isolated population in Wyoming. Outside the breeding season it may frequent pond, river, marsh and large margins more commonly than the *B. a. americanus*, in order to restore its water balance since it frequents a generally more arid climate. It hybridizes freely with *B. a. americanus* in a narrow zone in eastern Manitoba. Influence of this intermingling of characteristics can be detected for some distance east and west of this zone. It narrowly overlaps, but only rarely produces hybrids, with the Boreal Toad at its western limit along the foothills of the Rocky Mountains in southwestern Alberta and somewhat east of the Rockies in the Boreal Forest to the north.

Western Toad
Crapaud de l'Ouest
Bufo boreas

This is a large species over much of its range, and adult females may reach 127 mm in snout to vent length. In coloration these toads vary from grey, yellow, green, through browns, with darker blotches. The blotches are often more sharply contrasted with the background colour in females, and frequently have a tendency to join and form elongate patterns, which sometimes run irregularly almost the length of the body. The warts may contrast with the ground colour, and are often tipped with red. The underside is generally heavily speckled with black. The most striking identification feature is the absence of cranial and postorbital crests, though on some individuals very close examination will reveal extremely low, weak indications of their presence. There is a conspicuous

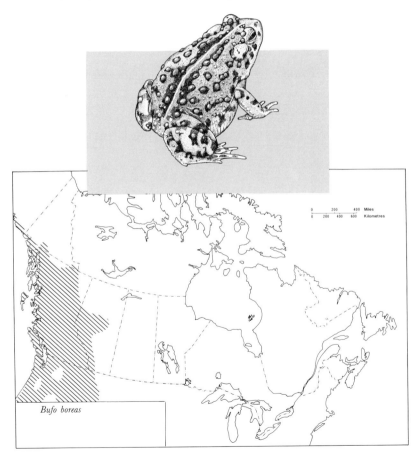

Bufo boreas

0   200   400   Miles
0   200   400   600   Kilometres

glandular fold of skin along the lower section of the hind leg (the tarsus) and extremely enlarged warts on the legs, sometimes extending nearly from knee to heel on the tibia.

The Boreal Toad ranges through both semi-arid and wet forested regions of British Columbia, north into southern Yukon Territory and along the coast of Alaska. In Alberta it does not range east of the Rocky Mountain foothills in the south, but in the Boreal Forest north of Edmonton, it extends east of that city. Where it meets the range of Canadian Toad the ranges overlap narrowly; the two may breed in the same ponds, and mismated pairs sometimes occur, very rarely producing hybrids.

Woodhouse's Toad
Crapaud de Woodhouse
Bufo woodhousei

This species is represented by one subspecies in Canada, Fowler's Toad, *Bufo woodhousei fowleri*. It is similar in appearance to the American Toad, although generally slightly smaller. Where their ranges overlap, identification can be made based on the following differences: Fowler's Toad generally has three or more warts per dorsal blotch while the southern *B. americanus* has only one or two; the postorbital crest of Fowler's Toad touches the anterior edge of the parotoid gland but in *B. americanus* the crest is clearly separated or touched by a backward spur of the crest; Fowler's Toad has an unspotted venter, or venter with only one prominent spot (pectoral spot) on the chest while *B. americanus* usually has more spotted venters covering one-third to the whole of the ventral region; in Fowler's Toad small warts are found on the upper surface of the tibia (the middle portion of the hind leg) while the same warts on the *B. americanus* are much larger.

The breeding call of males is also distinctive: the call is short in *B. w. fowleri*, about one to three seconds, but is much longer in *B. americanus*, lasting from four to 14 seconds, or even longer. Call duration varies somewhat with temperature; in both species it is usually the case of the warmer the toad, the shorter the call.

In Canada, Fowler's Toad is known only along the north shore of Lake Erie. It is a toad of sandy regions, and seems to prefer open areas. Where the American Toad occurs in the same area the

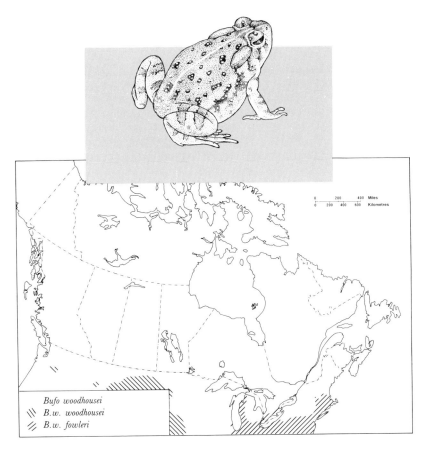

Bufo woodhousei
\\\ B.w. woodhousei
// B.w. fowleri

two may breed in the same pond and occasionally, hybrids, which are inter-mediate in call and morphological characters, are produced. Where they occur together *B. americanus* breeds earlier, in April and early May, where-as *B. w. fowleri* breeds in late May and June. There is some overlap, how-ever, and hybrid individuals often breed in May, between peak abundances of the parent species.

Great Plains Toad
Crapaud des steppes
Bufo cognatus

This is a large toad, attaining 114 mm in length. It has a strongly contrasted pattern of big dark blotches, each containing a large number of small warts, on a grey, brown or greenish background. The cranial crests are very heavy, uniting on the snout but strongly divergent posteriorly. Males have a peculiar vocal sac, appearing as a loose bit of black skin in the throat when at rest, but inflating to a large sausage-shaped structure, which bends up over the tip of the nose when the toad is calling. Other Canadian toads inflate the entire throat region to form a simple globular sac when calling.

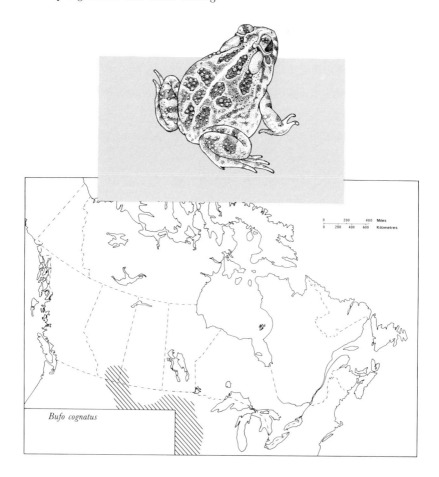

Bufo cognatus

The Great Plains Toad is an inhabitant of the short-grass prairie of southern Alberta and Saskatchewan. It breeds in response to heavy rains in late spring and early summer, congregating in sloughs, ditches and flooded fields. The deafening call has been likened to the sound of a pneumatic drill and may carry for 2 km over the treeless prairies.

Family Hylidae
Treefrogs

The family Hylidae includes 30 genera and 395 species, widespread through North, Central and South America but centred in tropical habitats. One genus, *Hyla*, occurs widely in Eurasia and the extreme northern edge of Africa but does not occur in India or most of the southern coast of Asia. The treefrogs of Australia and New Guinea are usually included with the Hylidae but it has been suggested that they should be placed in a separate family.

The Hylidae vary from minute forms less than 25 mm long as adults to "giant" species up to 140 mm in length. Usually they are slim-waisted and relatively long-legged with well-developed, circular toe discs for climbing. A small extra segment of the toe sets the discs off from the rest of the toe. Many species are arboreal (tree-dwelling) but they have also invaded grassland (particularly the genus *Pseudacris*) and margins of aquatic habitats *(Acris)*. Many tropical hylids have specialized breeding habits, including building mud basins at the edges of pools in which to lay their eggs, laying in water trapped at the base of arboreal epiphytic plants, laying in folded leaves, or carrying the eggs in a mass on the back of the female, or in a pouch formed by a fold of skin. The species that occur in Canada, however, all lay eggs in the open water of temporary or permanent ponds. They may be deposited singly along the submerged stem or leaves of aquatic vegetation or as small globular masses, depending on the species.

Hylid tadpoles of Canadian species have relatively deep tail fins, and the eyes generally protrude markedly from the side of the head. This is most evident when viewed from above. The middle part of the upper area around the mouth lacks papillae, and the tooth rows are usually two above the mouth and three below. In the Gray Treefrog complex, the deep red to light orange colour of the posterior half of the tadpole's tail distinguishes it from other species.

Transformation is in June through to August or even September in the latest breeding species (the Gray Treefrogs). Growth is rapid, and the young of early-breeding small species probably are ready to breed the year following transformation, though an additional summer's growth may be required in Gray Treefrogs.

Treefrogs eat a wide variety of insects and some other invertebrates, the types varying with the habitat, terrestrial or arboreal.

Male treefrogs inflate a dark balloon-like vocal sac that involves most of the throat area. The chin and throat are light or only lightly speckled in females. Often at the beginning or end of the breeding season, males will call from bushes or trees adjacent to the breeding pond. Some species will call during the summer in especially humid periods, such as before a rainstorm, or on a particularly warm fall day, from their non-breeding habitat, but usually this is a fainter and more muted call than the lusty volume produced during the breeding season. It is given with the vocal sac only partly inflated, while mating calls are produced with a fully inflated sac.

Spring Peeper
Rainette crucifère
Hyla crucifer

Although the adults of this small frog attain only 36 mm in length, the species has typical *Hyla* form and prominent toe discs. General coloration is light to dark brown, sometimes reddish, at least in the northern part of its range, with a prominent, darker cross-shaped marking on the back, though this may be variously broken into other configurations. There is a dark bar across the head between the eyes and a stripe from snout to tympanum. The markings may be indistinct on very light-coloured individuals and very bold on darker ones. Yellow is usually present in the groin area (normally covered when the legs are folded) and across rear of hind legs and vent. The underside is white, often with some dark flecking. The throat of the male is yellow, sometimes heavily overlain with dark pigment.

The call of these treefrogs is a shrill peep often rapidly repeated in territorial encounters between males. It may be heard from late March or April through to early July; peak choruses usually occur in April and May in southern Canada. Individual males will also call occasionally on dull days of late summer and early fall. Peepers range from Prince Edward Island to eastern Manitoba, generally occurring in wooded or bushy areas. They climb at least to the height of low bushes but are not as arboreal as the Gray Treefrogs.

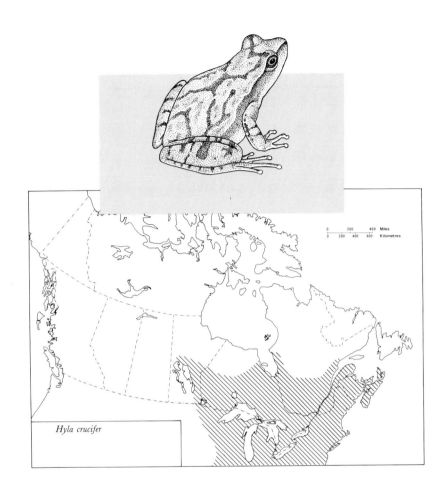

Hyla crucifer

0   200   400   Miles
0   200   400   600   Kilometres

Gray Treefrogs

These are the largest treefrogs found in Canada, reaching a length of 60 mm. They are frequently green, but may also be brown, or grey, with an irregular, often raggedly star-shaped, blotch on the back. A prominent light-coloured square is present under each eye. The groin and rear of the hind legs (surfaces that are hidden when the legs are folded in a normal sitting position) are bright orange to yellow with black mottling. This produces a "flash" coloration—it is not apparent until the frog leaps, exposing these areas, and is re-covered by the legs when it resumes a sitting position. The sudden flash of this contrasting colour is thought to confuse predators. The underside is unmarked white but males have a uniformly dark pigmented throat while females and juveniles may show a few flecks of black in this region. The brown-grey-green coloration is individually variable; one individual can change through these variations in response, at least in part, to activity or environment, often blending in perfectly with its background. Outside the breeding season, Gray Treefrogs forage in trees, though they are occasionally found on the ground. Sometimes they are attracted to the walls or windows of buildings at night if a light is luring a concentration of insects.

The two forms in the Gray Treefrog complex are indistinguishable in appearance but have completely distinctive calls; no intermediate calls are known. Experiments have shown that the females respond more actively to the call of their own species, and there is reduced fertility in laboratory crosses between the two species. Recently it has been shown that the eastern species is a tetraploid, having twice the number of chromosomes as occur in cells of the diploid western species.

Tetraploid Gray Treefrog
Rainette versicolore
Hyla versicolor

The Tetraploid Gray Treefrog occurs over southern Quebec, southern, central and northwestern Ontario and southeastern and central Manitoba. There is an isolated population in the vicinity of Fredericton, New Brunswick. Its call is a long, slow trill with individual pulses evident to the hearer.

Diploid Gray Treefrog
Rainette criarde
Hyla chrysoscelis

The Diploid Gray Treefrog, which occurs in south-central Manitoba, has a shorter, more raucous, fast trill in which the individual pulses are blurred together. The western species occurs in the southern Aspen Parkland and mixed forests of the region where colonies are often present in isolated "bluffs" of trees separated by stretches of bare

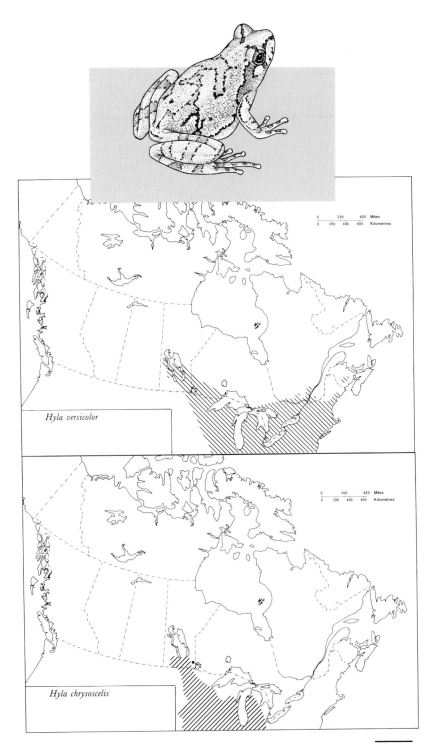

Hyla versicolor

Hyla chrysoscelis

grassland. Along the Red River and east of it there is a broad zone where the two species overlap. The calls of both species become shorter with increased temperature but even at the warmest *H. versicolor* has a slower, longer call than the coolest *chrysoscelis*.

Pacific Treefrog
Rainette du Pacifique
Hyla regilla

This western species is intermediate in size between Peepers and Gray Treefrogs, reaching a maximum length of about 51 mm. It may be black, grey, brown, tan or green and changes colour rapidly from light to dark. There is a prominent dark eye-stripe in all variations, and longitudinal stripes are often present on the back and sides. These stripes may be variously broken and vary greatly in intensity. The underside is cream and the hindquarters yellowish. In the mature male the throat is dark.

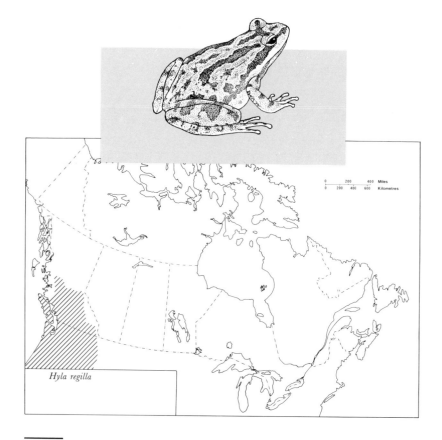

Hyla regilla

In Canada it occurs in southern mainland British Columbia and Vancouver Island, frequenting low plant growth and calling over an extended period from February on into the summer. It breeds in ditches, ponds, marshes, lakes and even slow streams. It is the only hylid within its range in British Columbia. Its distinctive "riv-et" call has been widely used in films for a tropical background and is commonly used in cartoons to typify a frog sound.

Striped Chorus Frog
Rainette faux-grillon
Pseudacris triseriata

This is a small species up to 38 mm in length, generally brown, but also red or green in the western subspecies. The pattern is variable but there is a prominent dark stripe through the eye,

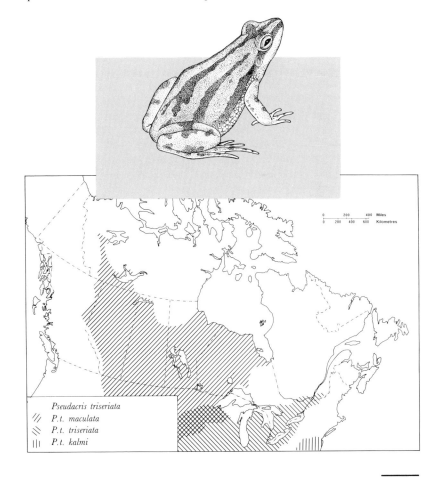

Pseudacris triseriata
/// P.t. maculata
\\\ P.t. triseriata
||| P.t. kalmi

which usually continues along the side of the body. Often three longitudinal stripes are present on the back but these may be variously interrupted and broken into dashes or spots, so that in some individuals all trace of the striping is lost and the spots appear randomly placed. Rarely, in the western race, there is a single broad stripe down the centre of the back. A dark marking, often triangular in shape, is usually present on the top of the head between the eyelids. The underside is a light cream colour. The body form and head are somewhat elongate, in contrast to the more compact, short-headed *Hyla*, and the legs are relatively much shorter. The toes are long and the toe discs small. The somewhat granular quality of the skin is particularly noticeable on the underside.

The call of the Chorus Frog is a drawn-out rasping, like the sound produced by drawing a thumbnail slowly over the teeth of a pocket comb.

Two subspecies of *Pseudacris triseriata* are recognized in Canada. The Midland Chorus Frog, *P. t. triseriata* occurs in southern Quebec and southern Ontario and has been introduced in Newfoundland. It is almost invariably some shade of brown, usually with striping patterns rather than spotted ones. The Boreal Chorus Frog, *P. t. maculata*, ranges across northern Ontario from James Bay, south to Lake Superior, and west throughout most of Manitoba and Saskatchewan and in Alberta to the foothills, into British Columbia in the Peace River region and north into the southern Mackenzie valley of the Northwest Territories. It is often spotted, or at least has the stripes broken up; green and red colour phases are common as well as brown, and it has relatively shorter hind legs.

Throughout its range the Chorus Frog is an inhabitant of open fields and clearings, and is extremely abundant throughout the prairie region. It rarely climbs above tall grasses. Both subspecies begin calling as soon as most of the winter's snow has melted and temperatures rise to the 5° to 10°C range or above on sunny days. The western race, however, will continue to breed until early summer in response to heavy rainfall, whereas the eastern form is generally silent after early June.

Northern Cricket Frog
Rainette grillon
Acris crepitans

This relatively large-headed small frog achieves a length of 35 mm, with an elongate snout, long hind legs and a generally warty appearance. The hind toes have extensive webbing with undeveloped toe discs. The Cricket Frog is usually brown or grey with a V-shaped dark marking on the head between the eyes and faint markings on the back.

The rear surface of the hind legs has a dark, ragged-edged stripe. It breeds in late spring, and the call has been likened to the clicking of pebbles in rapid succession. It is terrestrial and usually inhabits the margins of permanent water when disturbed. It takes cover in the water in a series of quick, erratic hops. In Canada, the subspecies, Blanchard's Cricket Frog, *A. c. blanchardi*, has been found only at Point Pelee and Pelee Island in extreme southwestern Ontario. Its continued existence at Point Pelee is doubtful, and studies on Pelee Island indicate it is declining in numbers there.

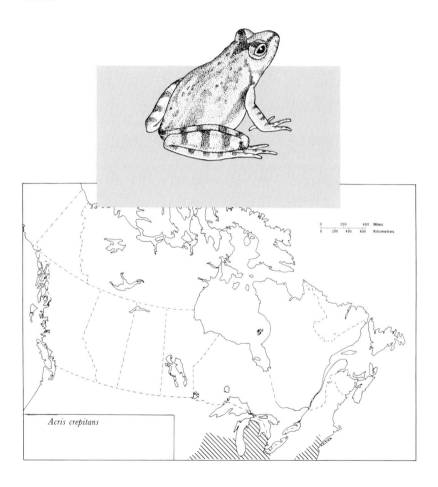

Acris crepitans

0   200   400   Miles
0   200   400   600   Kilometres

Family Ranidae
True Frogs

This large and diverse family includes 45 genera and 586 species. It is nearly worldwide in distribution, but is absent from all but the northern tip of Australia and from southern South America. Africa is a centre of diversity with at least five subfamilies represented.

The genus *Rana* is distributed over most of the range of the entire family, and is the only genus of ranid in Europe, northern Asia and North and South America. Of the eight species of *Rana* that occur in Canada, four were originally restricted to the east (though two have been introduced into British Columbia), two are restricted to the west, and two range from the Atlantic coast, through the Prairie Provinces and to British Columbia.

Rana species are typical frogs in build and life history. Some species have dorsolateral folds—raised folds along each side of the back running along most of the body length and occasionally shorter, raised folds between them on the back. The tympanum is always distinct, and in three of the species found in Canada (Bullfrog, Green Frog and Mink Frog) the tympanum of a mature male is much larger than that of the female. In the latter it is about the diameter of the frog's eye. No sexual difference in eardrum size is apparent in the other five species found in Canada. There are no parotoid glands, no toe discs, and no spades on the hind feet. The eye pupil is more-or-less round or horizontal, never vertical, and the hind toes have well-developed webs. In the Wood Frog male, at breeding, the hind toe webbing bulges out to be convex; in the female the webbing is concave as it is in all other Canadian *Rana*. In the male Wood Frog, the webbing shrinks to normal concavity after breeding. The males of all *Rana* have very dark basal swellings on their thumbs in the breeding season.

All Canadian species lay relatively large numbers of small-yolked eggs in open water. A typical tadpole, or polliwog, hatches from each egg. Like most anurans, *Rana* tadpoles have well-developed tail fins and chunky bodies. They are usually greenish, olive green or black, often with light or brassy flecks and some dark spotting or mottling. The belly is white to yellowish. The sides of the mouth are indented. The eyes are fairly close together, well within the outline of the head when viewed from above. Tooth rows are generally two to three above the mouth and three to four below.

These tadpoles are large, from 51 mm in the Wood Frog to 150 mm in total length in the Bullfrog. Developmental time is varied: most species complete their development the year of hatching but in Canada the Bullfrog apparently always overwinters at least one year as a tadpole. Some other species, such as the Green Frog and the Mink Frog, may do this regularly as well. These overwintering species usually breed in permanent water, such as large ponds, lakes and bays of rivers, where the ice does not reach the bottom, and the oxygen content remains sufficient all winter. Other species often lay their eggs in temporary ponds or in ponds that are shallow enough to freeze to the bottom in winter, and their tadpoles must transform within the summer. Generally, temporary pond breeders breed early in the year, permanent water breeders breed later. This, of course, is partly because smaller ponds warm up faster in the spring than do larger bodies of water.

Early breeders lay globular compact egg masses, attached to vegetation below the surface of the water; late breeders lay a film of eggs which spreads out on the surface of the water. This variation is apparently caused by available oxygen and temperature. In the cold water of early spring the amount of dissolved oxygen is high, and eggs even in the centre of a globular mass will receive an adequate supply for development. On the other hand, often the spring temperature drops to below freezing, and a film of ice may form over the surface. A mass below the surface is not exposed to such freezing. In late spring or summer, water temperatures rise and the amount of dissolved oxygen is less. A large globular mass below the surface would probably suffer inadequate oxygen in at least its inner layers. All eggs in a surface film receive adequate oxygen but because they have been laid later are not in danger of freezing.

Developing frog embryos have been shown to have upper and lower temperature limits, characteristic for each species, in which they will develop normally. Temperatures above or below these boundaries result in abnormalities or death. Among eastern species, the most northerly ranging species *(R. sylvatica)* has the lowest upper and lower developmental temperature limits, and the least northerly ranging species *(R. catesbeiana)* has the highest limiting temperatures.

Those frogs that breed in temporary ponds perhaps have a longer calling period. The males, at least of Bullfrogs and Green Frogs, establish breeding territories, often calling from them and defending them against the invasion of other males. This defence often takes the form of wrestling matches between the defending and intruding males. Coincident with territorial calls and the defence of territory is the greatly enlarged eardrum of males in these species.

Rana eat a variety of insects and other invertebrates; the adults of the larger species, especially Bullfrogs and Green Frogs, have occasionally been observed to consume small mammals and birds, as well as smaller frogs (even of their own species) and small snakes. Probably the only limit to what creatures a large Bullfrog will eat is prey size.

Rana in Canada can be divided, for identification, into three groups based on colour and pattern: the Brown Frogs, the Boldly Spotted Frogs and the Green Frogs.

Brown Frogs
Brown Frogs are dorsally always brown, grey or reddish but never green; all Brown Frogs have conspicuous dorsolateral folds and a dark mask that extends from the snout to over the eardrum on each side of the head.

Wood Frog
Grenouille des bois
Rana sylvatica
The smallest *Rana* rarely grows more than 65 mm in Canada, although it attains a larger size in the eastern United States. It is generally grey or brown, but may be distinctly red, especially in females, often with black spots on the sides and back. The underside is white, often with dusky mottling. The dark face mask is conspicuous. A phase with a prominent light stripe down the centre of the back is common in some populations in the north and west but very rare in the easternmost portion of the range. Any *Rana* in Canada with a light dorsal stripe is certainly a Wood Frog. The relative length of the legs is longer in the eastern frogs, shorter in the western frogs, but no subspecies are currently recognized. The call of the Wood Frog is a low, often rapid quack. It breeds as soon as ponds are free of ice in the spring, often starting when there are still patches of snow in the woods. The breeding may be concentrated in a very few nights and extend over only two weeks at one locality. In southern Ontario the Wood Frog will begin to call as early as March but in the north breeding may be delayed until late May or early June.

Wood Frogs extend further north than any other amphibian or reptile in the Western Hemisphere, occurring throughout eastern Canada, Manitoba, Saskatchewan, Alberta, in northern British Columbia and parts of the Yukon and Northwest Territories. They are absent from prairie areas. In general their range extends north to the tree line, and along the wooded Mackenzie valley, penetrates the Arctic Circle

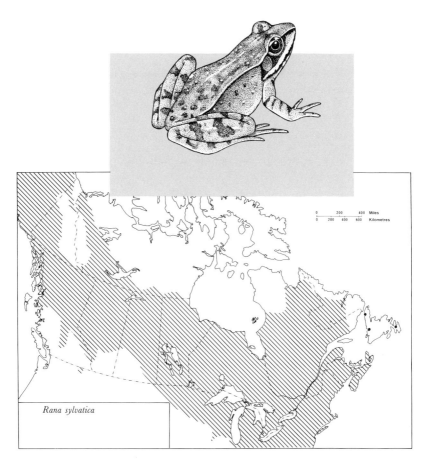

Rana sylvatica

and extends to the coast. The Wood Frog has been introduced into western Newfoundland at Corner Brook. After breeding, it usually disperses to damp woodland (hence the name, Wood Frog) though in the west and north it may often remain around pond margins and marshes for much of the summer.

Spotted Frog
Grenouille maculée
Rana pretiosa

This species is larger than the Wood Frog, and may reach a maximum size of 102 mm. Its dark facial mask is not as prominent as that of the Wood Frog. Usually there are irregular dark markings scattered over the back, often with light centres. The underside of adults is red or orange, (sometimes only over the posterior portion), occasionally covering almost all the ventral surface. Juveniles do not show any red colour and can easily be confused with young or adult Wood Frogs where the two overlap in range. Wood Frogs have shorter hind legs in the west than the Spotted Frog, the mask is more conspicuous, there is often a dorsal stripe and the spots do not have light centres.

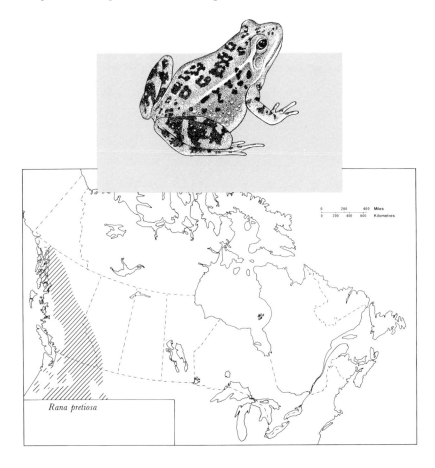

Rana pretiosa

The Spotted Frog is widely distributed throughout British Columbia but is absent from the extreme southwestern portion of the mainland (except for a narrow overlap with the range of the Red-legged Frog) and Vancouver Island. It also occurs along the Rocky Mountains in western Alberta. It is generally aquatic, inhabiting the margins of streams, rivers, marshes and lakes, but will move into adjacent woods and meadows to forage for insects and other invertebrates. The mating call has been described as a series of short bass notes, usually six to nine in sequence, but as few as four and as many as 26. Its volume is low and carries 20 to 30 m at most. In southwestern British Columbia, the Spotted Frog breeds in February and March, laying its egg masses in shallow water (not attached to vegetation). Often the masses of many females will be deposited on top of or adjacent to each other.

Tadpoles representative of major families of frogs in Canada. Top: Bufonidae *(Bufo americanus)*; middle; Hylidae *(Pseudacris triseriata)*; bottom: Ranidae *(Rana pipiens)*.

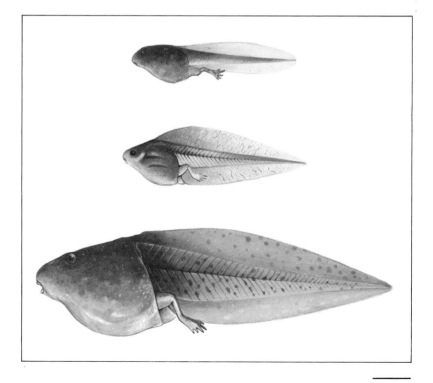

Red-legged Frog
Grenouille à pattes rouges
Rana aurora

The largest of the Brown Frogs found in Canada, the Red-legged Frog may reach a size of 127 mm. The black mask is not as prominent as in the Wood Frog, and the dark spotting on the back is made up of small black flecks and irregular larger blotches. The ground colour may be grey or reddish. Adults have extensive ventral areas of red, which may be lacking in juveniles who show yellow on the underside of hind legs and in the groin area (inside the rear leg insertion). The eyes are turned outward, and when viewed from above they are well covered by the eyelids (in the Spotted Frog the eyes are turned upward and are not as well covered by the eyelids). Red-legged Frogs have longer hind legs and a more slender, less chunky, appearance than the Spotted Frog.

Rana aurora

In Canada this species is restricted to the south-western portion of mainland British Columbia and Vancouver Island. It usually inhabits permanent marshes, lakes, ponds and quiet areas of streams, but it disperses into adjacent fields and woods after the breeding season. The call has been described as a low and gutteral "uh" usually repeated five or six times with a rise in emphasis on the last note of a series. It often calls underwater, and these sounds may be scarcely audible at the surface. Calls given above the water are heard no more than 10 m away. In southwestern British Columbia, the Red-legged Frog breeds in February and March; the egg masses are attached to submerged vegetation at depths from 26 to 130 cm usually half a metre or more apart from each other.

Boldly Spotted Frogs

The Boldly Spotted Frogs include the Leopard Frog and the Pickerel Frog: although most *Rana* are spotted to some extent, the two species included here have bold regular spots, which may be round or square, and which are evenly arranged over the back and sides. The light dorsolateral folds are prominent and contrast with the back colour. The eggs are laid as a loose mass, not as compact as in the Brown Frogs, and are often attached to submerged vegetation.

Northern Leopard Frog
Grenouille léopard
Rana pipiens

The spots are round or oval in outline with distinct light borders; adjacent spots may run together. In some specimens there are small dots, or reticulations, of black between the spots. This species is usually green but may also be brown or grey, with an unmarked milky-white underside. It grows to a maximum size of about 111 mm.

The Leopard Frog species complex is the most widely distributed anuran group in North America. The Northern Leopard Frog occurs from the Maritime Provinces, through much of Quebec and Ontario and across Manitoba, Saskatchewan and Alberta to the Rocky Mountains and even as far north as the Northwest Territories at Fort Smith. In British Columbia it is restricted to the southern valleys of the central and eastern regions but it has been introduced on Vancouver Island. It breeds in lakes, ponds, marshes and flooded areas of streams and rivers in the early spring, starting somewhat later than the Wood Frog. Its call is low-pitched and may be given underwater, but is more often given by frogs as they float spread-eagled on the surface. This call is perhaps best described as a long, drawn-out rattling snore, usually punctuated at the end with several rapid short grunts. A large chorus can sound like a perpetual droning. In summer these frogs commonly disperse widely into meadowlands and fields, particularly in low moist areas. In late fall they generally return to ponds, streams and rivers where they usually remain

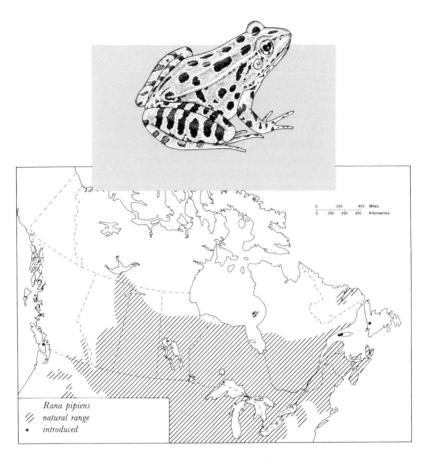

Rana pipiens
/// natural range
• introduced

more-or-less dormant on the bottom in winter. However, that they do move some is attested by their being caught in minnow-traps and gill nets used under the ice.

Leopard Frog tadpoles transform in July and August and occasionally as late as September and early October; they need more permanent water than the earlier breeding, faster transforming Wood Frog. Often, Leopard Frogs attempt to overwinter in ponds too shallow for their survival, and their bodies may be seen on the bottom in the spring as soon as the ice has melted. Either the pond freezes completely to the bottom, or the dissolved oxygen content of the water becomes too low for survival.

This species is widely used in university and high school biology courses for demonstrating the basic structure and physiology of vertebrate animals. Large numbers are taken by biological supply-house companies for sale to such institutions. In Canada, due to the rigours of the environment, which cause sudden crashes of population numbers, Leopard Frogs may not be capable of supporting sustained commercial exploitation.

Pickerel Frog
Grenouille des marais
Rana palustris

A smaller species than the Leopard Frog, the Pickerel Frog reaches a maximum length of about 87 mm. Its spots are square or rectangular, though often imperfect in outline, usually in two rows down the back, but a third, central row may be present on part of the back. Similar spots are present on the sides. The dorsolateral folds are prominent and brassy in coloration, even more accentuated than in the

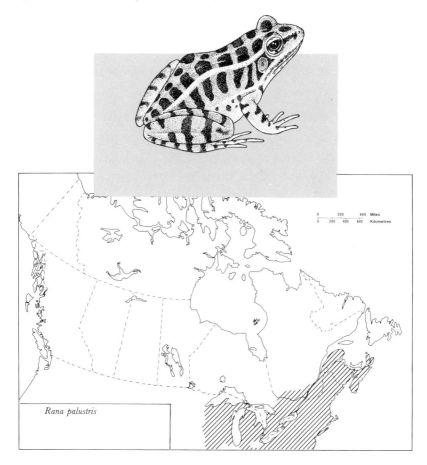

Rana palustris

Leopard Frog. Adults are bright yellow or yellow-orange on the underside of the hind legs, the groin and often, on the ventral surface. Newly transformed individuals are white underneath but soon acquire some yellow. Pickerel Frogs are always brown in ground colour, never green. Their skin-gland secretions may make them distasteful to some predators.

Pickerel Frogs occur in eastern Canada, mostly in Nova Scotia and New Brunswick. Some Ontario and western Quebec populations are declining, and at a few localities where they formerly were recorded they seem to have completely disappeared. The reasons for this decline are not known but modification of habitat from forest to farmland may be a factor. They seem to prefer clear, cool waters of forest, meadow streams and backwaters within eastern Canada, though they will forage into meadowland and fields. Pickerel Frogs are known to interbreed at least occasionally with Leopard Frogs. Where these two species use the same pond, or when the original landscape has been cleared, the Leopard Frog seems better able to survive.

Pickerel Frogs breed in the spring. The males produce a fairly short low-pitched snore that does not carry well. Often, males call underwater. Both this species and the Leopard Frog are widely used by bait fishermen, and the name "Pickerel Frog" probably originated from the custom of fishing for pickerel with it. (The Leopard Frog, however, apparently obtained its name from its spotted pattern.)

Green Frogs

Green Frogs may be green or brown, sometimes almost yellow-brown to black, but generally green predominates; the upper jaw is almost always distinctly green. They lack the prominent light line along the edge of the upper jaw to the front leg insertion that is present in both the Brown and the Spotted frogs. Although the Green Frogs are often spotted, these markings are indistinct and generally very irregular in outline, position and size. The eardrum diameter is greater than the eye diameter in mature males. Mature males have bright yellow throats (white in all other Canadian *Rana*). Dorsolateral folds are not as prominent, and are completely absent in the Bullfrog. The eggs are laid as a surface film, except in the Mink Frog, which lays an egg mass attached to submerged vegetation. The tadpole is more streamlined than in other Canadian *Rana*, with a lower tail fin.

Green Frog
Grenouille verte
Rana clamitans

The maximum size of this species is about 102 mm, and the coloration is extremely variable ranging through yellow, green, to nearly black. Commonly, at least the head and shoulders are

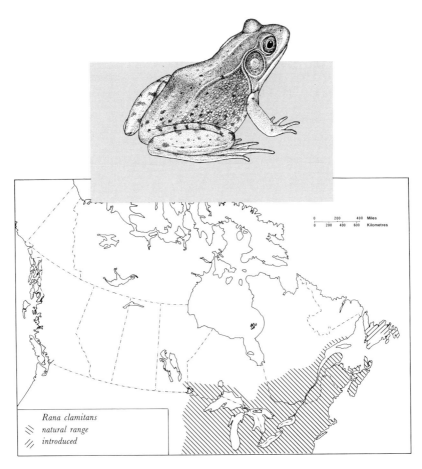

Rana clamitans
natural range
introduced

green. Dorsal spots are highly irregular in shape and distribution and may vary from abundant to none at all. The dorsolateral folds are fairly distinct and continue the length of the back. The hind legs are barred, with the marking at right angles across the long axis of the leg. Green Frogs occur widely in eastern Canada from Prince Edward Island to the Ontario–Manitoba border and have been introduced in southwestern British Columbia and in Newfoundland. The subspecies of Green Frog that occurs in Canada is *Rana clamitans melanota*.

The Green Frog breeds in a variety of sites: ditches, ponds and the bays of rivers and lakes. Usually, the tadpoles overwinter and transform early the following summer but sometimes they may transform in the late summer of the year in which the eggs were laid, if this was early enough. They breed in May, June and early July. Postbreeding adults and juveniles may follow streams and creeks away from the breeding areas to forage. The call is a distinctive "twang" or "chung," which has been likened to a note struck on a loose banjo string. The tadpole is moderately to heavily spotted or mottled above and white below.

Mink Frog
Grenouille du Nord
Rana septentrionalis

The Mink Frog reaches 76 mm in length. The head and shoulders are usually green and the back brown, but either green or brown may predominate. Large irregular dark spots and an elaborate pattern of reticulations are present on the back. The reticulations are most pronounced in adult females and are distinctive for identification of the species. There are irregular, elongate spots on the hind legs with their longest axis along the hind legs, in contrast to the transverse bars on the hind legs of the Green Frog. Hind-leg marking is the single best characteristic for distinguishing the two species where their ranges overlap. Green Frogs

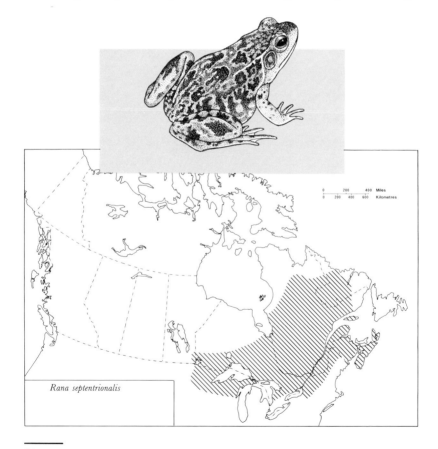

Rana septentrionalis

94

in these localities are often densely spotted and confusingly similar to Mink Frogs at first glance. The dorsolateral folds are often weak, sometimes absent, and rarely distinguishable more than a third to half-way down the body.

There is a distinctive odour of a freshly caught Mink Frog, said to resemble that of a mink by some and likened to rotting onions by others. It is the only frog species that emits a distinct smell. This odour is soon lost with handling, so the frog must be immediately checked for it when first caught. Mink Frogs are widely distributed through eastern Canada from Nova Scotia to New Brunswick and west to eastern Manitoba. They frequent permanent bodies of water, slow-moving streams, bog ponds and lakes, particularly where there is a dense surface mat of water lilies. They will sometimes forage away from such locations and turn up in temporary ponds and ditches.

Mink Frogs breed from May to July depending on latitude, and their call is a rapid, soft "took-took-took." The tadpole is very heavily mottled above and somewhat yellowish below. They overwinter and transform the next summer after hatching. The Mink Frog is usually extremely wary, and unless its habitat is approached carefully, the only indication of its presence is a skittering blur over the top of lily pads and a small splash in adjacent open waters. Patience usually will be rewarded by the eventual emergence of eyes and nose from the surface near the edge of a protecting lily pad.

Bullfrog
Ouaouaron
Rana catesbeiana
The Bullfrog is the giant, not only among Canadian, but among all North American frogs. Adults often reach a snout-vent length of 150 mm in Canada, and in the southern portion of their range Bullfrogs may attain 203 mm. They may be entirely green above, or green on the head and shoulders and brown on the back. Some individuals are virtually unspotted, others have scattered spots or dark mottling on the back. The underside is often mottled with grey. No dorsolateral folds are present on the body, but there is a prominent fold over the eardrum. The tadpole is spotted with small black dots over dorsal and lateral surfaces and may have a wash of yellow underneath.

Bullfrogs range through southern Ontario, Quebec, New Brunswick and Nova Scotia, and have been introduced in southwestern mainland British Columbia and Vancouver Island. They generally inhabit permanent waters of river bays, lakes and large ponds, but may forage a short distance from water in rainy periods and wander

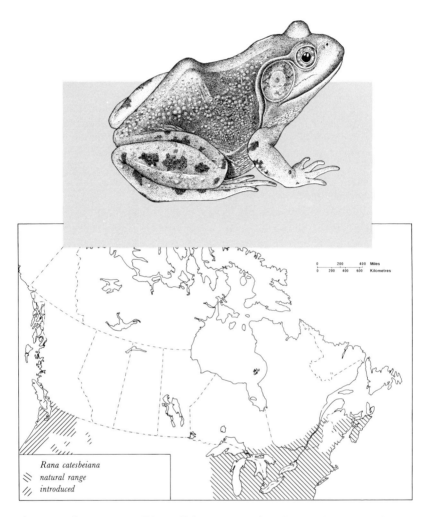

Rana catesbeiana
natural range
introduced

along smaller streams. The call is a resounding, bass, ''jug-o'-rum'' or ''oua-oua-ran,'' thought to resemble the bellowing of a bull by some, when given at peak intensity.

Bullfrogs are sometimes hunted for the supposed culinary virtues of their meaty hind legs. In Ontario such persecution has produced a decline in some populations, and comprehensive regulations governing the season and the size of the catch on hunting Bullfrogs have recently been passed. Information on current regulations can be obtained from the Ontario government. Because of its size it is also a favourite for dissection demonstrations in university and high school biology courses.

Order Testudines
Turtles

The turtles, terrapins and tortoises comprise the order Testudines, represented today by 11 families containing 72 genera and 222 species. Two of these families contain only marine species, and the remainder have largely freshwater or terrestrial species. Fossil turtles first appear in the deposits of the late Triassic and were distinctive even then. Their evolutionary origin is still controversial. The dorsal (carapace) and ventral (plastron) shells are usually bony and fused along the sides to each other. Internally, the backbone and expanded ribs fuse with the underside of the carapace. Turtles lack teeth, but have an efficient sharp-edged horny beak for biting off chunks of food. All turtles lay eggs in nest cavities that they dig with their hind feet, in soft, often sandy, soil. The eggs are covered and left unguarded, and when the young emerge they fend entirely for themselves. Many species have a mixed diet and are partly carnivorous, either catching invertebrates or small vertebrates alive, or scavenging from dead animals. Few are strictly vegetarians.

The terms *turtle, terrapin* and *tortoise* are confusingly applied, generally without regard to family classification. An attempt was once made to restrict the term *terrapin* to freshwater, especially edible, species, *tortoise* to the strictly terrestrial forms and *turtle* to marine species, but this arrangement is rarely followed. *Turtle* is usually used as an inclusive term for any representative of the order.

Turtle families are divided into two suborders: the Pleurodira and the Cryptodira. The Pleurodira contains two families of "side-necked" and "snake-necked" turtles that pull their necks in laterally (horizontally) and fold them across the front of the body under the protecting anterior lips of the shell so that the side of the head is showing underneath. These are represented in South America, Africa and Australia. A member of this group, the South American *Podocnemis*, used to be sold occasionally in North American pet stores as small juveniles. The sale of pet store aquatic turtles is now banned in Canada because these often harbour the bacterium, *Salmonella*, which is readily communicable to humans from contaminated turtles or the water they are kept in.

All other living turtles are placed in the suborder Cryptodira. They pull their necks into their shells vertically, in a more-or-less S-shaped curve, so that their heads face directly out nose-first when their necks are fully withdrawn. Four of the ten non-marine families in this group occur in Canada, and are represented by ten species. However, two of these, the Box Turtle and the Western Pond Turtle, are probably introduced.

Canadian species generally lay their eggs in late May, June and occasionally as late as early July. The young turtles hatch in the late summer and early fall and may dig out of the nest at this time.

Incubation time varies with the species, the site and the summer temperatures. In cool summers, at some localities, there is evidence that the young of certain species remain in the nest until the following spring before emerging. Unhatched eggs have also been found in the late fall and early spring (generally Snapping Turtle eggs), but it is unlikely that these eggs suspend development over winter and eventually hatch. They probably represent clutches laid too late to complete development before winter temperatures kill the embryos.

Family Chelydridae
Snapping Turtles

This family contains only two genera, each with one species, restricted to North and Central America. These are large turtles with ridged, or "keeled," carapaces and disproportionally large heads. The plastron is greatly reduced and cross-shaped, leaving the large muscular legs more exposed underneath but with more freedom of movement than in conventionally built turtles. The tail is relatively long. They are aggressive and outstandingly ugly in temperament when defending themselves on land where they are most vulnerable to attack. In water they usually slip quietly away from potential danger. The Alligator Snapping Turtle of the southeastern United States may weigh up to 100 kg but individual Common Snapping Turtles seldom weigh more than 10 kg; 22.5 kg is apparently the Canadian record weight.

Common Snapping Turtle
Chélydre serpentine
Chelydra serpentina

Despite the many claims of larger size, the record shell length (measured in a *straight line* from anterior to posterior margins of the shell and not along the curve of the shell) is 470 mm. The large head, long tail and the reduced, cross-shaped plastron serve to quickly identify Snappers from all other turtles. The saw-toothed appearance of the upper side of the tail, produced by a series of bony plates along it, is also distinctive. There are fleshy projections (barbels) on the chin. The general coloration of the carapace ranges from light brown to almost black. Adults are usually thickly covered above with a growth of algae, not only giving them a green coloration, but also obscuring the scutes (large scales) of the carapace. The underside is yellowish sprinkled with dark flecks, and the head, limbs and tail are brown. Light longitudinal lines may be evident on the sides of the head, but often are obscure. The young are darker in coloration.

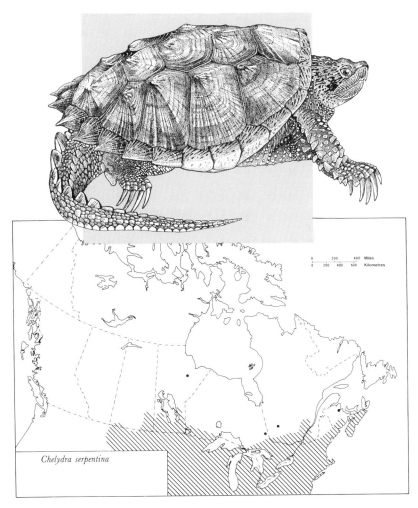

Chelydra serpentina

Snappers occur widely in southern, eastern and central Canada from Nova Scotia to Saskatchewan. They inhabit a variety of aquatic habitats—ponds, marshes, rivers and lakes—foraging in shallows barely deep enough to cover them. They will crawl out on fallen trees or rocks to bask in the sun but are not often seen doing this. The females are most often found on land when they are searching for an egg-laying site. Snapping Turtles are generally aggressively defensive, and because of their sharp and powerful jaws it is unwise to poke fingers or toes at them.

The neck is surprisingly long, enabling the Snapper to reach at least half the length of its shell. The eggs are round and resemble ping-pong balls. Usually 20 to 40 are laid but as many as 83 have been recorded from a single female.

Snapping Turtles eat a wide variety of animal and plant food including fish, frogs, birds and mammals. They consume few game fish, but do occasionally take ducklings, which they grab from below as the birds swim along the surface. Because they are good scavengers, and consume a large number of dead animals, they are generally more of a benefit than a liability where they occur. Snapping Turtles are trapped in some areas and eaten or sold for food; intensive trapping may reduce local populations.

Family Kinosternidae
Musk and Mud Turtles

These small and somewhat secretive turtles are highly aquatic and are rarely seen out of water except during the nesting season and while on occasional wanderings during rainy weather. They have a strong musky odour, released from secretions from glandular openings where the skin joins the underside of the carapace. Only four genera are recognized in the family, and the 22 included species range from South to North America but are best represented in Central America.

Stinkpot
Tortue musquée
Sternotherus odoratus

The relatively high-domed, narrow shell of this turtle is small, not exceeding 137 mm in length. It is brown above, flecked or streaked with black. The head, limbs and tail are dark above, and two yellowish lines are generally evident on each side of the head. The plastron is yellowish, somewhat reduced in size and does not fill the opening of the carapace; the moveable anterior lobe has a transverse hinge between the second and third pairs of plastral scutes. The male has large areas of skin between the plastral scutes and a thick tail with a horny nail at the tip; the female has only small areas of skin between the plastral scutes, with a short tail lacking a sharp tip. The scales around the edges of the plastron (the marginal scutes) number 23 (11 on each side plus a centre anterior one, the nuchal). Chin and throat barbels are present.

This turtle occurs in Canada only in southern Ontario generally in shallow, clear water of lakes, ponds and rivers. It can climb slanted overhanging trees along the water's edge to a height of at least 2 m above the water's surface. Like the Snapping Turtle, its shell

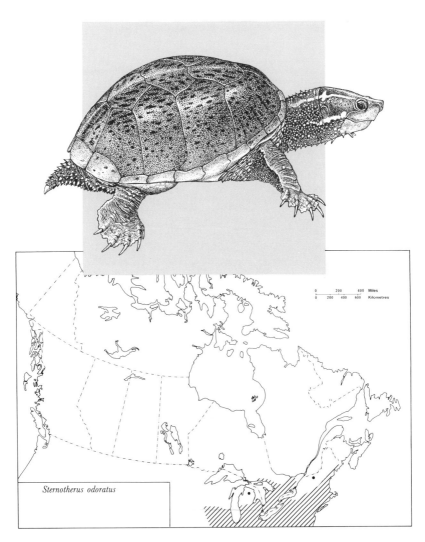

Sternotherus odoratus

may become covered with algae. The Stinkpot normally lays two to five eggs, and sometimes a nest cavity is not dug, but a female, or several together, may lay under logs along the shorelines, or even in the walls of muskrat houses. The food includes a wide variety of invertebrates, such as aquatic insects, crayfish, earthworms, molluscs and minnows, tadpoles and vegetation.

Family Emydidae
Pond and Marsh Turtles

This family of 28 genera and 80 species occurs in Europe, Asia, northern Africa, North, Central and South America. Some authorities also group the 10 genera and 39 species of strictly land-dwelling tortoises together with this freshwater group in the family Testudinidae, and give the largely aquatic members subfamily rank (Emydinae). Together, they are the largest group of living turtles. They have unreduced carapaces and plastrons with well-developed bridges joining them. There are generally 12 marginal scales on each side of the carapace, a total of 25 around the entire upper edge of the shell, including the nuchal. The shells are sometimes brightly patterned and often the head or limbs have red, orange or yellow, as solid colours or as markings. In Canada, five genera are represented, including seven species, one with three distinctive races. However, only four genera and five species are regarded as native.

Painted Turtle
Tortue peinte
Chrysemys picta

This is a brightly coloured species with a black to greenish carapace, margined and sometimes marked or streaked with yellow or red; the head, neck, limbs and tail are boldly striped with red and/or yellow. The yellow plastron may have no marks, may have a central dark marking, or may have an extensive and elaborate dark and red figure that extends along the seams of the scutes to the edge of the shell.

Three subspecies occur in Canada: the Eastern Painted Turtle, *C. p. picta*, typically has broad, light carapace scute margins, and the margins of the central and lateral rows of scutes line up with each other across the shell. The yellow undershell is usually plain without markings. The eastern race is reported from Nova Scotia and southern New Brunswick, but these populations seem to show some influence of past intergradation (interbreeding) with the Midland Painted Turtle; many maritime individuals have the central markings on the undershells and somewhat disaligned carapace scute margins, both characteristics of the Midland Painted Turtle. Further analysis may decide if the Painted Turtles of this region would be better designated *C. p. picta* × *marginata*.

The Midland Painted Turtle, *C. p. marginata*, has disaligned, or staggered, light scute margins of the central and lateral series of the carapace, and the margins themselves are narrower. Like the preceding subspecies, the head and top of the tail are striped with red, and the neck, limbs and lower surface of tail with yellow. Both show a red stripe down the centre of the carapace. The upper margins and lower surfaces of the marginal scutes of the carapace are boldly marked with red. There

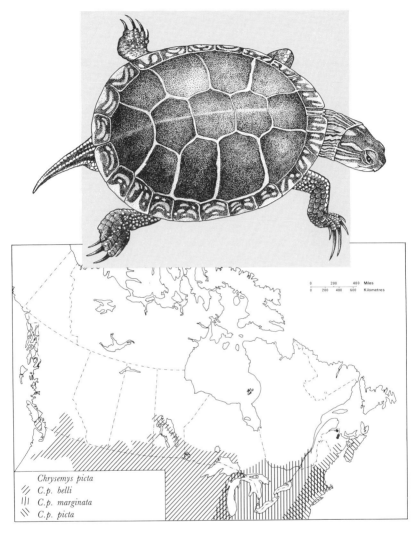

Chrysemys picta
/// C.p. belli
||| C.p. marginata
\\\ C.p. picta

is a dark central marking on the plastron, which is variable in size, and may be uniform or have red spots or streaks in it. This race occurs in southern Quebec and Ontario. In the western part of its range (toward Sault Ste. Marie) it may show the influence of intergradation with the western subspecies.

The Western Painted Turtle, *C. p. belli*, is the largest of the Painted Turtles, attaining a shell length of 251 mm. It has a flatter carapace with mostly yellow markings and an irregular pattern of lines tending to form an elaborate network. Large males are often marked with black reticulations on the carapace. The margins of the carapace scutes are disaligned. The plastron has a large, often intricately patterned, dark and red central marking, which extends out along the seams of the scutes. This race occurs over the southern portion of northwestern Ontario, Manitoba and Saskatchewan, and has been recorded once in Alberta, in the Milk River drainage of the southeastern portion of the province. It also occurs in the southern interior of British Columbia and on Vancouver Island.

Painted turtles are generally the most abundant turtles wherever they occur in Canada, and frequent ponds, marshes, rivers and lakes. They bask conspicuously on logs, stones and stumps projecting above the water, and on the banks if these objects are not available, sometimes piling one on top of the other if prime sunning sites are limited. They lay two to 20 eggs.

Map Turtle
Tortue géographique
Graptemys geographica

A relatively large turtle, adult females of this species attain a shell length of 273 mm, but males are much smaller. The carapace is somewhat flattened and low, with a slight dorsal keel (distinguishing this species from the Painted Turtle), with small knob-like backward projections conspicuous in juveniles and males but faint in large females. The hind feet are large and somewhat paddle-like. There is an elaborate pattern of yellow lines on the brown carapace, which suggests a map of waterways to some viewers (hence the common name). These markings become more obscure with increasing size. The head, neck, limbs and tail are dark and prominently marked with yellow lines. The plastron is plain yellow.

The Map Turtle occurs in southern Ontario and southwestern Quebec and seems to prefer larger bodies of water, such as rivers and lakes. It often basks, but usually chooses projecting objects in deep water. It is exceptionally wary and quickly dives when approached. Molluscs are its preferred food, but insects, crayfish, fish and some plant material are also taken. Clutch size usually varies from 10 to 16 eggs.

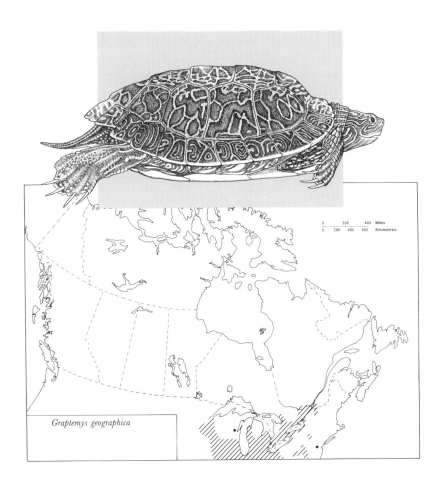

Graptemys geographica

0　　　200　　　400　　Miles
0　　200　　400　　600　　Kilometres

Blanding's Turtle
Tortue mouchetée
Emydoidea blandingi

This fairly large (up to 268 mm long) turtle with a high-domed carapace is generally black and profusely marked with dots or short streaks of yellow. The top of the head, the neck, limbs and tail are dark and unpatterned but the chin and throat are bright yellow, which distinguishes it from all other turtles in Canada. The adult plastron is yellow marked with black squares; in juveniles it is largely black except for a yellow edge. The Blanding's Turtle is sometimes called the semi-box turtle because of a hinge on the plastron that permits the partial closure of its anterior lobe. It occurs in southern Ontario and adjacent Quebec, with a disjunct, relict population in southwestern Nova Scotia.

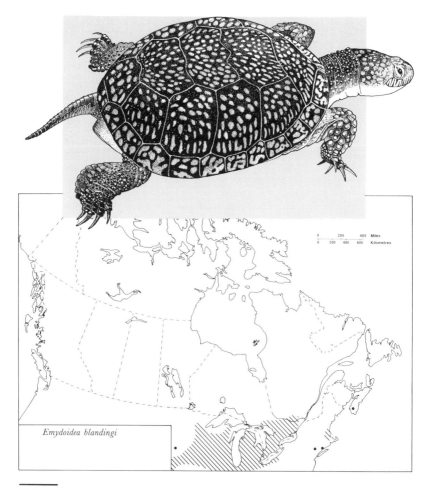

Emydoidea blandingi

Mainly aquatic, it is usually found in lakes and marshes, often in boggy areas. It feeds largely on crustaceans and insects, with some fish, snails, leeches and plants also taken. It lays from six to 11 eggs.

Wood Turtle
Tortue des bois
Clemmys insculpta

This turtle attains a total shell length of 229 mm. Its carapace is brown, and each scute shows prominent growth rings, giving it a rough appearance. The head and limbs are generally dark brown with

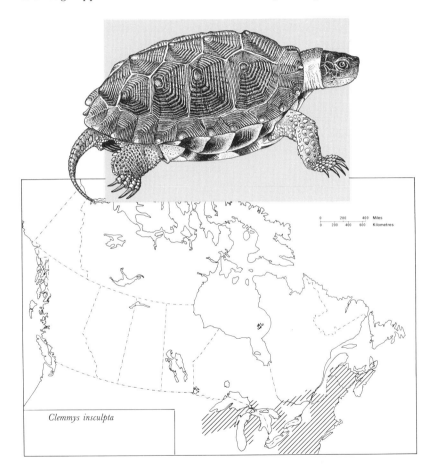

Clemmys insculpta

an orange or reddish suffusion. The plastron is yellow with black squares, similar in pattern to that of Blanding's Turtle.

The Wood Turtle occurs in Ontario, Quebec, New Brunswick and Nova Scotia in areas where its apparent restriction to sandy or gravelly bedded rivers gives it a somewhat erratic distribution. It will wander on land during the summer and is the most terrestrial of Canadian turtles except for the Box Turtle. Food includes a variety of plant material—filamentous algae, willow leaves and berries, particularly strawberries; and animals—insects, molluscs, crayfish, earthworms and tadpoles. Clutch size is between four and 12 eggs.

Spotted Turtle
Tortue ponctuée
Clemmys guttata

The smallest turtle in Canada, the Spotted Turtle does not exceed 127 mm in shell length. The carapace is black, with bright yellow or orange circular spots, the plastron yellowish with black blotches. In some individuals these blotches may be extensive and almost cover the plastral surface. The head, neck, limbs and tail are grey to black, usually marked with yellow. There is a band of yellow along each side of the head. The male has dark jaws; the female yellowish jaws.

In Canada it occurs in marshes and ponds in southwestern Ontario, where its numbers appear to have declined, and also in small lakes and bog ponds in southern Quebec and in eastern Ontario where it has only recently been discovered. It is fairly secretive, sometimes quick to take cover when approached, and most likely to be seen in spring before new growth of pond and marsh vegetation provides concealment. It seems at home both in water and on land and eats snails, slugs, worms, insects, frogs and filamentous green algae. Clutch size is from three to five eggs.

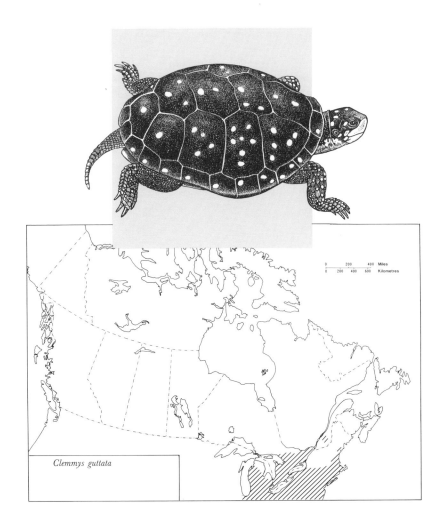

Clemmys guttata

Western Pond Turtle
Tortue de l'Ouest
Clemmys marmorata

This species may reach 178 mm in carapace length. It is blackish-brown to olive in colour with darker spots, or broken lines, radiating from the centres of the carapace scutes. The head, neck and limbs are dark with spots or outlining of black. The plastron is yellowish, usually with dark blotches. It has been recorded in 1933, 1936 and 1959 from British Columbia in the Vancouver region. Because some people

favour this turtle as food, and the only reports of it are from Vancouver, it is likely that they are based on escaped or released captives taken in the United States, rather than a native population. It feeds on both animals and plants including insects, worms, crustaceans and waterlilies.

Eastern Box Turtle
Tortue tabatière
Terrapene carolina

Maximum size of the Eastern Box Turtle has been recorded at 198 mm. This terrestrial turtle has a high, domed carapace and two hinges across the plastron allowing the anterior and posterior ends to be folded tightly against the underside of the carapace to give maximum protection to the head, limbs and tail: hence the name Box Turtle. Its colour is highly variable, both with age and size but also between individuals of comparable age and size. Generally it is black or brown with yellow or orange crescents, bars, blotches or other large irregular markings. The head, neck, limbs and tail are dark, black to brown, marked with streaks or spots of orange or yellow. The plastron is brown, often with dark blotches.

In Canada the Box Turtle has been recorded several times from Point Pelee, at least twice from Pelee Island and a couple of times elsewhere in southwestern Ontario, all in recent years. However, earlier investigations of these areas did not yield reports of it. This turtle is abundant in the United States, commonly wanders onto highways, and is often kept as a pet. It is likely that recent records are released or escaped pets of tourists. Excavations of Indian sites in southwestern Ontario have yielded several Box Turtle shells, which were prized for making ceremonial rattles. These shells may have been from natural Box Turtle populations occurring in the area in pre-European times but they could also have been obtained in trade with southern Indians. Box Turtles eat vegetation including mushrooms, berries and leaves, and animals including beetles, snails, slugs, crayfish and caterpillars, and even small amphibians, reptiles and carcasses of dead animals.

Family Trionychidae
Softshell Turtles

This very distinctive widespread family, found in North America, Africa and Asia, contains seven genera and 23 species. The appearance of these turtles has been likened to a pancake, as they have flat almost circular carapaces, covered with a leathery skin instead of horny scutes. The nose is elongated, tubelike, the neck long, and the hind feet somewhat paddle-like. A single species occurs in Canada.

Spiny Softshell
Tortue–molle à épines
Trionyx spiniferus

Large females attain a carapace length of 432 mm, males are smaller. The carapace is greenish grey to brown. The dark-edged, light-centred spots of the juveniles are retained in males, but replaced by brown blotches in females. The dark head, neck, limbs and tail are streaked or spotted with light. The plastron is yellowish. The carapace in the male is covered with tiny spines; it is generally smooth in females except for spines along the anterior edge. In Canada, Softshells have been recorded from southern Ontario and Quebec. They occur mainly in the Ottawa, St. Lawrence and Richelieu rivers and in Lake Erie, particularly

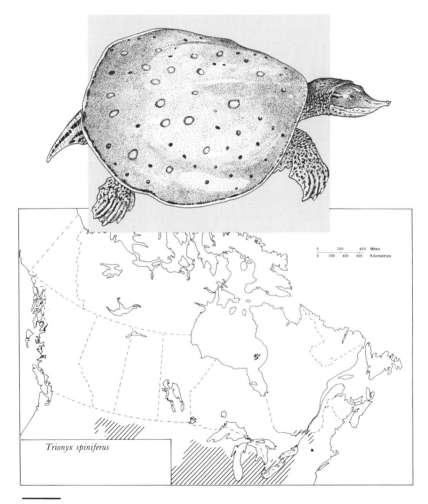

Trionyx spiniferus

where sand or mud bars are present. They are mostly carnivorous, eating crayfish, and aquatic insects and some fish. Clutch size is four to 32 eggs. Softshells are difficult to capture, as they rarely can be found basking in the open and are exceedingly wary. If captured they are savage in disposition. They often lie in shallow water with the shell covered in sand or mud, extending their long necks to bring the nostrils just above the surface for air.

Families Dermochelyidae and Cheloniidae – Marine Turtles

Only seven species of marine turtles exist today but they are widely distributed through the warm oceanic areas of the world. They also appear regularly in some northern areas in summer. Four genera (six or seven species) are included in the family Cheloniidae. A single genus containing a unique species is placed in family Dermochelyidae.

Marine turtles greatly exceed their freshwater contemporaries in size. All marine turtles have modified, paddle-like flippers, which distinguish them from all freshwater forms. Marine turtles do not reproduce in Canada; nesting of all species is confined to beaches of warmer areas. The individuals sighted off Canadian coasts are either waifs carried north of their main range by ocean currents, or they are part of a summer feeding migration. As yet, it has not been discovered if any of these northern wanderers eventually find their way south again to breed and lay eggs. Marine turtles do not come ashore, except for basking Pacific Green Turtles and nesting females of all species.

The survival of all marine turtle species is threatened. Large numbers of eggs are collected for food, and many beaches where nesting formerly took place on a large scale have suffered drastic reductions in the numbers of laying females. Both at nesting beaches and in the sea, adult marine turtles, except for the Leatherback, are sought and taken for food. Marine turtles are also exploited for skins for leather and, in the case of the otherwise commercially unattractive Leatherback, for oils used in cosmetics. Young turtles, stuffed and coated with lacquer, find a ready tourist market in the Caribbean area, in Mexico and elsewhere as souvenirs. One species, the Hawksbill (which has not been yet recorded in Canadian waters) was prized for its shell from which "tortoiseshell" hair combs and other ornaments were made. The manufacture of substitutes, first of celluloid, then of plastic, almost completely eradicated this use for a time, easing the pressure on Hawksbill populations. However, with the more recent popularity of authentic or natural ornaments, a renewal of persecution has begun.

Many countries now have taken steps to monitor and protect certain important nesting beaches, and research on reproduction and movements of marine turtles has been supported. The

Convention on International Trade in Endangered Species of Wild Fauna and Flora now forbids the importation of all marine turtles into or out of Canada, except under permit.

In Canada, there apparently has never been any commercial exploitation. Smaller specimens are sometimes taken aboard offshore fishing boats but are generally released, and the capture of larger individuals is rarely attempted. Turtles that are brought ashore are usually ones that have become entangled in fishing gear or harpooned by inshore fishermen. These are generally exhibited as curiosities for a time and infrequently kept as trophies.

Family Dermochelyidae

Leatherback Turtle
Tortue luth
Dermochelys coriacea
This is the largest living species of turtle; record size is obscured by variable techniques of measurement and weight estimates, but it can grow to a carapace length of 183 cm and attain a weight of 680 kg. Its carapace is without scutes and is covered with smooth, brownish, slaty, or bluish black skin above; white predominates below. There are five longitudinal ridges on the carapace, one on each side, and five on the plastron, most conspicuous on young individuals. Irregular spots or patches of white or pink may be present on the shell and on the brown-to-black head, neck and limbs.

The Leatherback is primarily a pelagic (open ocean) marine species but will sometimes enter shallow bays and estuaries. It is distributed throughout the tropical waters of the Atlantic, Pacific and Indian oceans and has been recorded north to Norway, the British Isles, Labrador, British Columbia and Japan; south to Argentina, Chile, Australia and the Cape of Good Hope. It also enters the Mediterranean Sea. Nesting in the western North Atlantic has not been recorded north of South Carolina.

The Atlantic form has been recorded in the Bay of Fundy, the Atlantic coast of Nova Scotia, in the Northumberland Strait off New Brunswick, and off the eastern coast of Newfoundland on a regular basis from June to October with a peak abundance in August. It also has been found off the mid-Labrador coast near Nain. Records for the Pacific form are more infrequent, but it has been observed at Nootka Sound, in the vicinity of Barkley Sound, off Esperanza Inlet, Brooks Bay, Uslero Inlet and in Sedgwick Bay (Queen Charlotte Islands), and ranges north to southern Alaska.

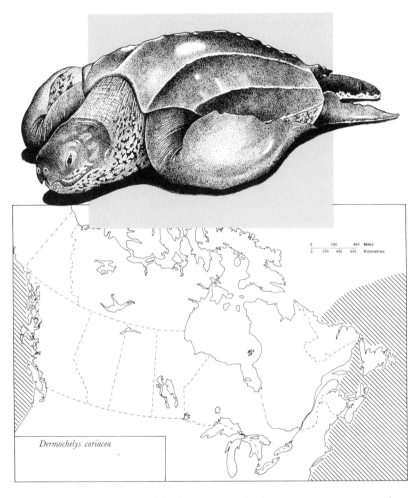

Dermochelys coriacea

Their more northerly occurrence compared to other sea turtles may be because of an apparent ability to maintain body temperature of 25°C when in sea water as much as 18°C cooler. This is probably due to an ability to retain heat generated by muscle activity facilitated by the Leatherback's large mass in proportion to its surface area.

Jellyfish have been recorded as a major food source for Leatherbacks: large, soft, backward-projecting spines in the oesophagus may help to hold and swallow this slippery prey.

Family Cheloniidae

Only four genera represent these typical sea turtles: *Caretta*, the huge Loggerheads: *Chelonia*, the Green Turtles: *Eretmochelys*, the Hawksbills, and *Lepidochelys*, the Ridleys. *Caretta* and *Lepidochelys* occur in Canadian Atlantic waters, and the *Chelonia* has been recorded off Pacific Canada.

Loggerhead Turtle
Caouane
Caretta caretta

One of the largest of the hard-shelled turtles, the Loggerhead attains a carapace length of at least 122 cm and a weight of over 227 kg. Much greater weights have been suggested by estimation from large skulls in museum collections. Its distinctive reddish brown carapace has five or more large costal scutes bordering the centre row on each side, the first of these always touching the centre anterior scute (the nuchal) of the marginal series (the smaller scutes that border the carapace). Three (usually) or four large scutes are present on the bridge between the upper and lower shells. All these scutes are without pores.

The Loggerhead ranges over the Pacific, Indian and Atlantic oceans from the British Isles, Nova Scotia, southern California and Japan to Chile, Australia, southern Africa and Argentina. It wanders widely, as far as 300 km into the open sea, but also enters a variety of coastal bays, lagoons and river mouths. It nests as far north as North Carolina on the Atlantic coast, but rarely, in the past, has nested on Maryland and New Jersey beaches. Only the Atlantic subspecies *C. c. caretta* has been recorded off Canada. Most specimens landed in Canada have been taken in the warm waters of the Gulf Stream of the George's Bank area where Canadian fishing trawlers go as far south as Cape Hatteras. One Loggerhead, however, was taken 4.8 km off Devils Island, Halifax County, Nova Scotia, and another just off Chebucto Head, near Halifax.

Loggerheads are carnivorous; algae and other vegetation found in their stomachs may be taken only incidentally while they feed on animals associated with marine vegetation. Individuals captured inshore in Canada are suspected to have been carried in on the eddies

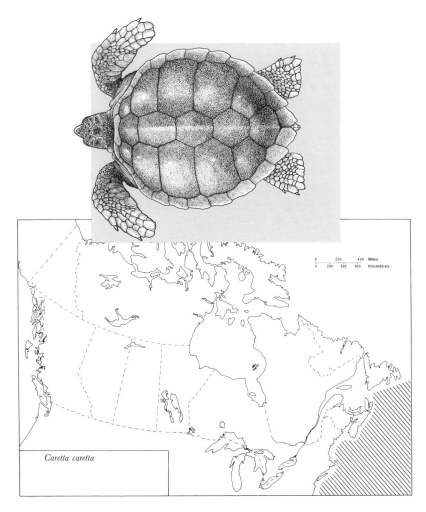

Caretta caretta

of the Gulf Stream. Such eddies may have drifted away from the main current and later dissipated and mixed with cold coastal currents leaving the turtles benumbed. This contrasts with the occurrence of active Leatherbacks in these areas, probably because they are able to maintain a body temperature significantly higher than that of the water they are in.

Atlantic Ridley
Tortue bâtarde
Lepidochelys kempi

This relatively small species among marine turtles attains a maximum length of 74.9 cm and a weight of only 49.9 kg. The almost circular carapace is olive-green to grey to pale yellow in coloration. The plastron is yellow. Five costal shields are present on

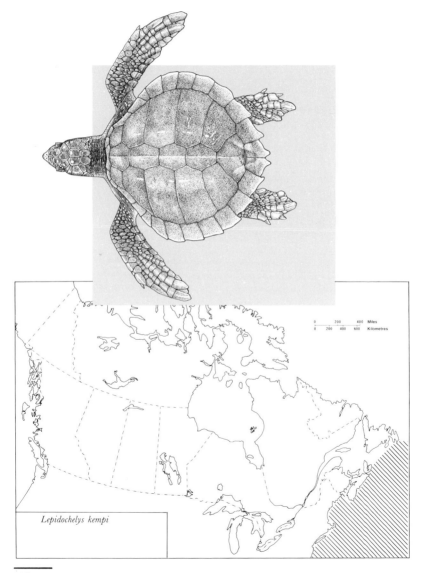

Lepidochelys kempi

each side of the central row of shields on the carapace. The first touches the nuchal, the anterior, central scute, in the series of smaller marginal scutes that form the border of the carapace. Usually there are four (very rarely five) large scales on the bridge between carapace and plastron. Each of these scales has a distinct pore near its posterior edge.

The Atlantic Ridley occurs in the western Atlantic Ocean from Nova Scotia and Newfoundland to Bermuda and Mexico. It also has been recorded off the British Isles, Scilly, France and the Azores, and in the Mediterranean Sea. Canadian records are from the southeast coast of Newfoundland near St. Mary's Bay and off Nova Scotia in the Bay of Fundy near Margaretsville, Annapolis County; Spry Harbour, Halifax County; and Lahave Island, Lunenburg County. It apparently prefers shallow water and is primarily carnivorous. It nests along the Gulf of Mexico.

In the folklore of Caribbean natives and fishermen, who knew of no nesting areas for the Ridley, it was long regarded as a hybrid between Loggerhead and Green turtles and commonly referred to by the rude term indicating the offspring of an unauthorized liaison. Because of its limited distribution, and particularly its restricted nesting area, the Atlantic Ridley is in a more precarious position for continued survival than other marine turtles. There is also a distinct Pacific species of Ridley, but it does not range north to Canada.

Green Turtle
Tortue verte
Chelonia mydas

Green Turtles attain a carapace length of at least 140 cm and a weight of 295 kg and thus may exceed the size of Loggerheads unless estimates of even larger specimens of the latter species from museum specimens are valid. The common name is derived from the colour of the greenish body fat, not the external colour. The carapace is brown to olive with dark mottlings, radiations or blotches often visible. The plastron is unpatterned pale yellow to whitish. Head and limbs are brown. The smooth carapace has four costal scutes on each side of the central row of vertebral scutes. The first costal never touches the nuchal scute (the anterior centre scute of the small marginal scutes that border the carapace).

The Green Turtle occurs in the Pacific, Altantic and Indian oceans, largely in tropical areas. In the Atlantic it has been definitely recorded only as far north as Massachusetts. Only in the Pacific has it been recorded off Canada. The sole Canadian record is from Spring Cove, west side of the entrance to Ucluelet Inlet, Clayoquot District, Vancouver Island, but it has also been recorded in southern coastal Alaska.

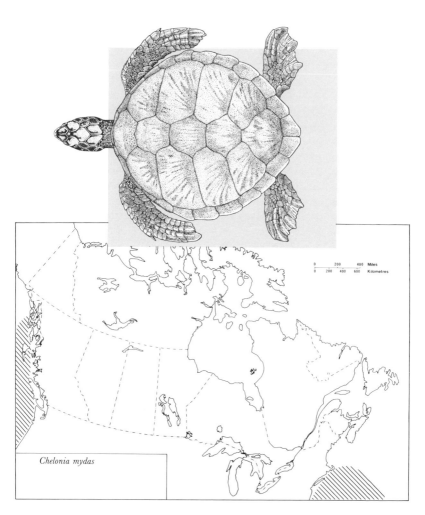

Chelonia mydas

The favourite habitat for this turtle is the shallow waters of shoals where an abundance of vegetation is present. It has long been prized as food by man both for its flesh and for the "calipee" and "calipash" derived from cartilaginous portions of the shell and used in green-turtle soup.

Order Squamata:
Suborder Lacertilia – Lizards

Lizards are the most abundant reptiles in the world today, and 3307 species are recognized (compared to 2267 snakes, the next largest group). Lizards and snakes, together with the lizard-like Amphisbaenids, (135 species) form the Order Squamata of the Reptilia.

All lizards have scales, in contrast to the often similarly shaped salamanders, which have unscaled, glandular skins common to amphibians. Lizards usually possess third eyelids (nictitating membranes) and external ears, both of which snakes lack. Many lizards readily lose their tails and grow new ones; snakes do not. However, many species have greatly reduced legs, or none at all, giving them the general appearance of snakes. The dividing line between the two groups is almost bridged by some primitive, but still existing, families.

Lizards are most diverse and abundant in the tropics. In North America the centre of their abundance and diversity is the southwest. They have not spread very successfully into the northern regions of North America: the five species (one with two subspecies) recorded in Canada are generally confined to the southern, warmest, portions of the country. Snakes and, to a lesser extent, turtles have been far more successful in penetrating north on the American continent. The same is not true for Europe and Asia where the first reptiles to drop out as one moves northward are turtles, and where a lizard, *Lacerta vivipara*, which bears its young alive, ranges to north of the Arctic Circle.

Lizards have adapted to a great variety of habitats: they live at the ground surface, below it, and above it in trees. One species is a highly successful glider (the Flying Dragon, *Draco*, of Asia). Some regularly frequent fresh water and one readily enters salt water to feed on algae (the Marine Iguana of the Galapagos Islands).

In size lizards range from the ponderous Komodo Dragon *(Varanus komodoensis)*, which may attain a length of 3 m, to small active forms a few centimetres long at maximum adult size. They may be dorsally flattened as the pancake-like desert-dwelling Horned Lizards *(Phrynosoma)*, or laterally flattened like chameleons of the African tropical forests. Some are burrowers in the sand and resemble small snakes, others run on their hind legs like miniature dinosaurs. They may be totally herbivorous, or wholly carnivorous, eating anything from minute insects to birds and mammals. They may be spiny as are the horned lizards or smooth like the skinks.

Only two species of lizards are poisonous: the Gila Monster *(Heloderma suspectum)*, and the Mexican Beaded Lizard *(Heloderma horridum)* of the southwestern United States and Mexico. These chunky, short-tailed, clumsy appearing beasts may reach a total length of 900 mm. Their venom glands, in the lower jaw, are unconnected with the teeth, unlike those of poisonous snakes, but they have a tendency to chew on a bitten object, and grooves in the teeth aid the poison to flow from the lizard's mouth to the wound. Bites are seldom fatal to humans, but can be very painful.

Eighteen families of lizards have living representatives, and at least six additional families are recognized from fossils. Canada has representatives of three of the extant families.

Family Iguanidae

This large family of lizards contains 55 genera and 608 species. Although it occurs primarily in the Americas, three genera—two in Madagascar and one in the Fiji and Tonga Islands—represent it in the remainder of the world. It includes such well-known forms as the Iguana, several species of basilisk and the anoles (or American Chameleons) all so often displayed in pet stores. These are largely tropical species and usually waste away from starvation and pneumonia in Canadian homes unless given special care including draft-free, heated quarters and abundant supplies of food. Of this family, the only native representative to Canada is the Horned Lizard.

Short-horned Lizard
Iguane à petites cornes
Phrynosoma douglassi

This squat, flattened little lizard with a wide body and shortened tail grows to a maximum length of 114 mm. The entire back, sides and upper surfaces of the legs are covered with small spines. The flat, bony head has short, stubby, dagger-like spines (horns) projecting back from its rear fringe. The scales on the undersurfaces are smooth. It is yellowish, brown or grey on the back with dark brown, light bordered, blotches. The venter is white to yellowish.

Two subspecies have been recorded in Canada. The Eastern Short-horned Lizard, *P. d. brevirostre*, occurs in the short-grass prairie of southeastern Alberta and in the vicinity of the Frenchman River valley of southwestern Saskatchewan. It often has dorsal spots with indistinct borders, or with borders only along their posterior edges. The Pigmy Lizard, *P. d. douglassi*, has been recorded solely in the arid southern Okanagan valley of British Columbia, near Osoyoos at the American border. The only collection was made late in the last century. It is darker in coloration and has shorter horns.

Horned lizards are exceptionally difficult to find. Although they are abroad in the daytime, often in bare, frequently sandy areas, they generally sit tight when approached and depend on their markings and spiny skin to conceal them effectively. They seem most abundant

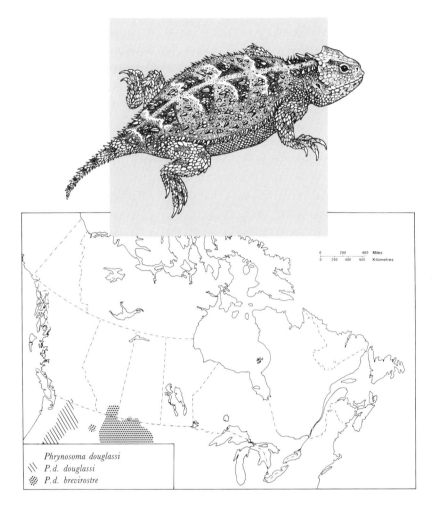

Phrynosoma douglassi
\\\ P.d. douglassi
❋ P.d. brevirostre

in Alberta along south-facing coulees (prairie ravines) but are rarely observed even during intensive searchings. They eat insects, particularly ants. Horned lizards are often kept as pets but it is difficult to supply them with the heat and large quantities of ants they require to remain healthy. Unfortunately their naturally flat shape and ability to fast for long periods partially disguises the fact that they are wasting away in captivity until they are dead.

Horned Lizards possess the rarely observed ability to rupture a blood vessel at the base of their third eyelid and actually squirt blood from the eye. This has been suggested to be a chemical defence against predators, as the taste of this blood is thought to discourage further interest even by a hungry coyote. Short-horned Lizards bear live young, sometimes as many as three dozen in a single litter.

Family Anguidae
Alligator Lizards

This is a small family of six genera and 74 species, but it has representatives over the Americas, West Indies, Europe, Asia and North Africa. Included are the legless Slow Worms *(Anguis)* of Europe, Asia and northern Africa, and the Glass Lizards *(Ophisaurus)* of eastern and central North America, Europe, Asia and northern Africa. The Alligator Lizards *(Gerrhonotus)* occur in western North America and have well-developed but short limbs, slender bodies and long tails.

Northern Alligator Lizard
Lézard–alligator boréal
Gerrhonotus coeruleus

Lizards in the genus *Gerrhonotus* have a prominent fold along each side of the body separating the relatively large square, bone-reinforced back and belly scales with a flexible area of granular scales, which may serve to allow expansion when breathing, feeding or carrying young. The Northern Alligator Lizard attains a total length of up to 229 mm, and it is the largest lizard found in Canada. Its back is brown with irregular dark spots, and the sides greyish. The underside is white with a yellowish or greenish hue. The tail breaks readily, but a replacement section, usually darker than the original, is re-grown.

This lizard occurs in southern British Columbia, along the lower coast and in southern Vancouver Island. It frequents dry woodland and sometimes grassland, often in rocky areas with a stream or spring nearby. It is usually found under bark, logs and stones but may also be seen in the open. It eats insects and spiders but also takes snails and millipedes. It is live-bearing, producing litters of up to 15 young. The subspecies, *G. c. principis*, is the only representative in Canada.

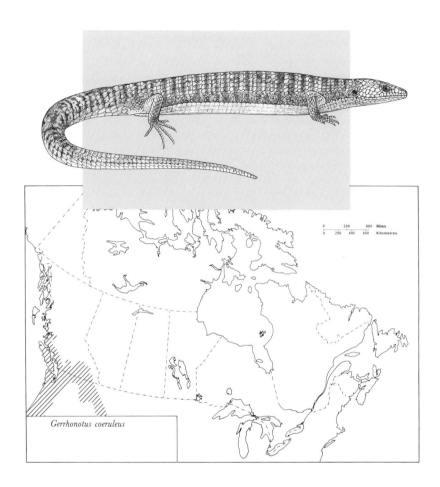

Gerrhonotus coeruleus

Family Scincidae
Skinks

Skinks are a large, worldwide family of medium to small-sized lizards generally with smooth polished-looking scales. Eighty-five genera and 1029 species are recognized. They are most plentiful in Africa, southern Asia, the west Pacific Islands and Australia, and less diverse on the American continent. Three species, all in the genus *Eumeces*, range into eastern, central and western Canada. All show a pattern of light longitudinal stripes on a dark background; the stripes are most vivid on the young. Most species tend to darken somewhat with age, and males in particular may lose much of the juvenile distinctiveness of their pattern. Mature males have red or orange coloration on the sides of the head during the breeding season. The bright blue tails of the Canadian species, when young, become duller with age, and finally turn grey. The tail breaks readily, and its brighter colour and thrashing after breaking may serve to distract a predator's attention from the duller-coloured skink itself, allowing it to escape.

Their diet consists of insects, spiders, sowbugs and other terrestrial invertebrates. Skinks lay eggs in somewhat moist locations, such as the interior of a rotting log. The female may guard the eggs until they hatch. Skinks are extremely active, foraging during the day and taking shelter under stones, logs and similar cover. Usually their preferred habitat has some moisture, a stream, swamp or spring nearby, but they are most often seen or found under cover, in the adjacent dry portions.

Five-lined Skink
Scinque pentaligne
Eumeces fasciatus

This skink attains a maximum length of about 205 mm. It has five white-to-yellowish stripes on a black ground colour when young, but this pattern becomes obscure with age; the stripes darken and the ground colour lightens.

In Canada it occurs only in southern Ontario, well within the Great Lakes forest region, where it is recorded north to the Georgian Bay area and east to the vicinity of Snow Road and Palmerston Lake near Perth. It is often locally abundant where it occurs but is not continuous in distribution. In the northern part of its range it occurs on the rocky outcroppings of the pre-Cambrian Canadian Shield, but it seems more abundant to the south, along the sandy peninsulas of Lake Erie, such as Point Pelee.

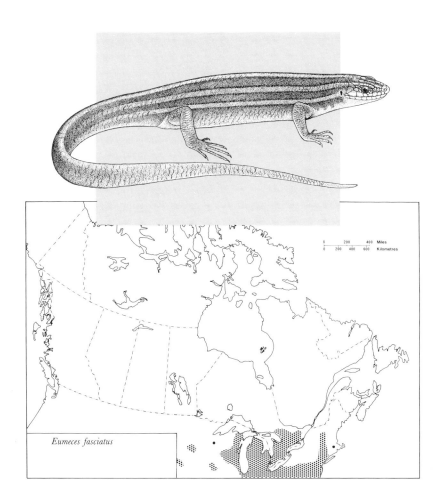

Eumeces fasciatus

Prairie Skink
Scinque des Prairies
Eumeces septentrionalis

The Prairie Skink, which grows to a length of 206 mm, generally has seven light stripes. On the sides these are strongly bordered by dark stripes above and beneath, but the back stripes tend to be bordered by fainter dark lines. The general ground colour is olive verging toward brown. The dorsal striping particularly tends to be obscure on larger individuals.

The Canadian subspecies is the Northern Prairie Skink, *E. s. septentrionalis*, and is restricted to the sandy area near Shilo and the Spruce Woods Provincial Park east of Brandon in southwestern

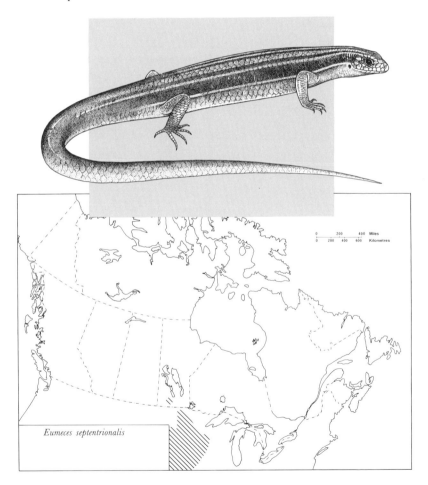

Eumeces septentrionalis

Manitoba. The light soils in these areas may allow it to burrow deeply enough to escape the winter frost whereas the surrounding heavier clay soils do not. The Canadian localities seem to be disjunct from the continuous range of the species, which ends in southwestern North Dakota and northeastern Minnesota.

Western Skink
Scinque de l'Ouest
Eumeces skiltonianus

The maximum length of the Western Skink is about 179 mm. Two pale stripes, bluish grey or whitish, run the length

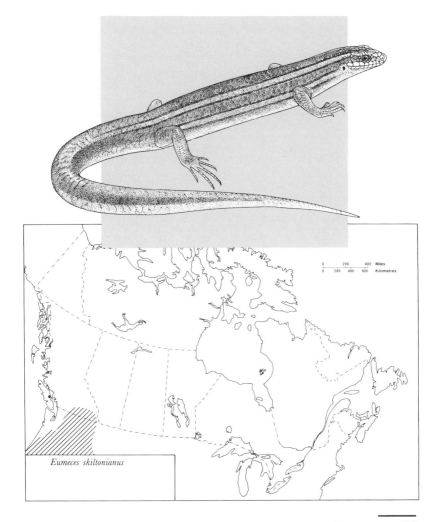

Eumeces skiltonianus

of the body on each side, and continue onto the sides of the head. The back is brown edged with black along the upper edge of the first lateral stripe. The ground colour of the sides is brown to black.

In Canada the Western Skink occurs in southern central British Columbia. It may also occur on Vancouver Island from where there are old reports and one recent sight record that seems almost certainly to have been this species. It can be found both in grassland and forest, and on dry hillsides.

Order Squamata:
Suborder Serpentes – Snakes

Probably no other group of vertebrate animals in the world ranks close to snakes for arousing strong emotions ranging from fascination to terror in man. The 12 families of living snakes are divided into three infraorders: the Scolecophidae contains three families of small burrowing species (Typhlopidae, Leptotyphlopidae, Anomalepidae); the Henophidia contains the boas (Boidae), the wart snakes (Acrochordidae) and three families of aberrant burrowing forms (Aniliidae, Uropeltidae and Xenopeltidae); and the Caenophidia contains all the "advanced" snakes including 85% of living snake species (Colubridae, the harmless and rear-fanged snakes; Elapidae, the cobras, mambas and coral snakes; Hydrophiidae, the sea snakes; and Viperidae, the vipers and the pit vipers).

Twenty-four species of snakes occur in Canada, and three families are represented. The Boidae has one small species in British Columbia (the Rubber Boa, *Charina bottae*). The Colubridae, which includes the abundant and widespread garter snakes, is the best represented with 20 species. Both of these families contain only harmless species, although all have needle-sharp, backward-projecting teeth, which can inflict a skin-puncturing bite. The smallest species can barely penetrate human skin with their teeth, but larger kinds, such as the Rat Snakes *(Elaphe)* and Gopher Snakes *(Pituophis)*, can cause bleeding. Only three species of Canadian snakes, all rattlesnakes, are poisonous. Two are recorded in southern Ontario (one of these is now believed to be extinct) and the other occurs in the arid regions of southern Saskatchewan, Alberta and British Columbia. The remainder of the country is without dangerous species.

All snakes are legless, but some (such as the Boidae) retain vestiges of pelvic limb girdles. In snakes the body organs are elongated, and there are a great many vertebrae—from 141 to 435. In the more advanced snakes the left lung is much smaller than the right or even completely absent. The skull is specialized, and advanced forms have elastic attachments at the joints of the halves of the lower jaw where they attach to the skull, allowing them to swallow prey much larger than their own diameter. Snakes are scaled but the skin between the scales of the neck and body can be stretched to accommodate large prey. To avoid choking, they can extend a special breathing tube during the slow process of engulfing large prey. The tongue of snakes is forked at the tip and can be extended some distance beyond the mouth. By licking particles from the air with its tongue, and flicking the tongue back into cavities in the roof of the mouth (Jacobson's organs), a snake receives a sensation of smell. Snakes are constantly testing their surroundings by flicking their tongues in and out. The tongue is not a stinger as some folklore would designate it. The poison of snakes is injected by enlarged grooved or hollow upper teeth, which are connected to poison glands.

Snakes have radiated into a variety of habitats: marine, freshwater, terrestrial, fossorial (underground) and arboreal, and are found all over the world except in the polar regions. They may be either live-bearing or egg-laying. They always prey on other animals, none are herbivorous. As a group they have a variety of prey—invertebrates, amphibians, reptiles (including other snakes), birds, their eggs and mammals, but individual species often specialize in a particular prey type.

Family Boidae
Boas and Pythons

The more sensational members of this family are relatively well-publicized giants among snakes. The Anaconda *(Eunectes murinus)* of South America and Trinidad, and the Reticulate Python *(Python reticulatus)* of southwestern Asia both reach lengths of 10 m. The Boa Constrictor *(Boa constrictor)* of South and Central America is much smaller, growing to about 6 m in length. Three other species are intermediate in size: the Indian Python *(Python molurus)*, the African Python *(Python sebae)* and the Amethystine Python *(Liasis amethystinus)* of northern Australia, all reach lengths of about 7 m. There are many other members of the family, but none approach the giants, which are so often thought of whenever the boas are mentioned.

There are 18 genera and 58 species of boas, all largely tropical in distribution. Boidae are known as fossils from 60 million years ago, and one extinct form, *Gigantophis*, has been estimated to have reached 20 m in length. Most have rudiments of the pelvic girdle and vestiges of hind limbs, which appear as small claws, usually larger in males than females, and which have a function in courtship. These snakes largely feed on warm-blooded animals (birds and mammals), wrapping several loops of their body around their prey. The steady tightening of these loops every time the enveloped animal breathes out soon compresses its lungs to the point where further breathing is impossible, and death is rapid. The prey is subsequently swallowed whole at leisure. This is an exceedingly effective means of subduing a toothed, often clawed, active prey that otherwise could inflict mortal damage to a predator like a snake, which lacks the limbs or the tearing teeth or beaks that birds of prey and mammalian carnivores use to subdue their food.

Canada's representative of the family is the Rubber Boa, a small and secretive member in the subfamily Erycinae. The subfamily includes two genera found in western North America, one in Africa and Asia and one in the East Indies. They are short-tailed, small-eyed, mainly burrowing forms.

Rubber Boa
Boa caoutchouc
Charina bottae

This boa only reaches a maximum length of 73.7 cm. It is greyish- to yellowish-brown above and yellow below, unmarked or with a few dark flecks along the sides. Its tail is short and blunt, and its ventral (belly) scales are relatively narrow compared to those in other snakes found in Canada. The smooth dorsal scales and wrinkled skin give it a rubbery appearance. In Canada it occurs in southern British Columbia and frequents grassland and forest particularly in sandy or loam soil. It is secretive, mainly nocturnal and frequently burrows, though it can also swim and climb well. It is generally sluggish in contrast to the quick, alert colubrids that comprise most of our snake fauna. The Rubber Boa may roll into a ball, often with the head hidden and the blunt tail end exposed. It is sometimes called the "two-headed snake," an allusion to the difficulty of telling the ends apart. It is thought to feed largely on birds and mammals, which it kills by constriction. It is live-bearing, producing two to eight young in a litter.

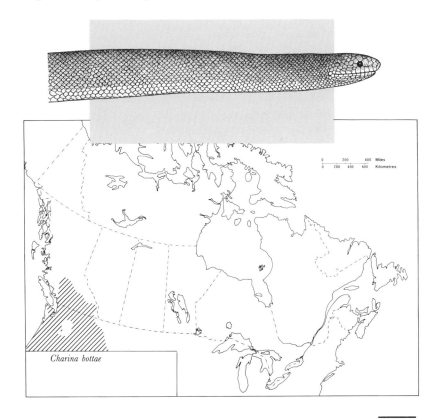

Charina bottae

Family Colubridae
Typical Snakes

The family Colubridae contains the majority of snake species, represented by 291 genera and 1550 species distributed throughout the world. A few Southern Hemisphere species have enlarged rear fangs and are poisonous, but all Canadian species are harmless. For convenience of discussion they have been divided artificially here into three groups: the abundant garter and water snakes, the smaller harmless species, and the larger harmless species.

Garter Snakes and Water Snakes

The most abundant, widely distributed, and commonly seen snakes in Canada belong to three closely related genera in the subfamily Natricinae of the family Colubridae. These are the garter snakes (genus *Thamnophis*) and the water snakes (genera *Nerodia* and *Regina*). These are generalized, active snakes, usually of medium size. The subfamily Natricinae is widespread and occurs in Europe, Asia, Africa, North America and northern Australia. *Nerodia* and *Thamnophis* are restricted to North and Central America, *Regina* to North America.

Nerodia is generally heavy bodied and primarily aquatic. *Regina* is more slender and generally aquatic. *Thamnophis* is often terrestrial, but many primarily aquatic species occur, particularly in western North America where *Nerodia* and *Regina* are absent. *Nerodia* and *Regina* have a divided anal scale (the scale just anterior to the vent on the underside of snakes, which marks the point where the body ends and the tail begins). In *Thamnophis* the anal scale is undivided.

All species in these genera are live-bearing in North America (in contrast to species of the genus *Natrix* in Eurasia which lay eggs). Litter size may be huge: the Common Garter Snake, *Thamnophis sirtalis*, has been recorded to bear as many as 85 young. Normally, however, litter size is less than 40. Generally larger females have more young, but there is some evidence that with advancing age litter size may decline. As in all the snakes, the young are independent from birth and receive no parental care. Although persistent folklore states that in times of acute danger the mother will open her mouth to let the young take refuge there, this has never been observed under captive conditions, nor confirmed by the numerous scientists investigating snake behaviour in natural conditions. The myth is likely based in part on the cannibalistic tendencies of some snakes and on the speed with which newborn snakes can take cover and seemingly disappear.

Mating occurs mostly in the early spring, when snakes emerge from hibernation, though it has also been observed in the fall just before hibernation. The young are generally born in late summer or early fall. In some localities these snakes den up communally for the winter in particularly suitable, usually rocky, areas where there are cracks and crevices leading from the surface well below the winter frost-line. In Manitoba, dens estimated to be used by as many as 10 000 snakes have been studied. These are most typical of northern portions of the range where suitable wintering sites may be limited. Where summer is shorter it is probably advantageous for individuals to cluster for spring mating and thus minimize time wasted on searching for mates, and maximize chances for embryos to complete development and for the young to be born within one summer. In southern Canada the tendency to den in large numbers appears less pronounced or lacking.

Growth is rapid, and young snakes may be mature by their second fall. These snakes feed on a variety of prey. Earthworms are relished by some garter snakes especially by the young. Other invertebrates, salamanders, frogs and fish are also eaten. The larger garter snakes will eat birds and small mammals at least occasionally. These snakes usually grab their prey and swallow it whole with little effort to subdue it. Prey is generally taken head first, an advantage with long-limbed victims such as frogs, as the legs can be neatly pressed backward as they are engulfed. In common with other snakes, these species have small, needle-sharp, backward-projecting teeth, ideally suited for holding struggling and often slippery prey.

Usually these snakes dart quickly away whenever approached. However, if surprised or irritable, they may hold their ground, flatten their body and even strike out. Although they lack poison, large individuals can easily pierce a person's skin with their sharp teeth, usually leaving several marks no larger than pinpricks. Because of the bacteria in their mouths, occasionally a bite from one of these snakes will cause redness and mild swelling. Often people are distressed at sharing their yards and outbuildings with snakes: the only answer is to seal up holes where snakes hide (preferably while the snakes are away) and to remove the snakes themselves. There is no repellent known that is effective in discouraging these animals. Napthalene flakes (mothballs) are sometimes recommended for the purpose but are not effective, and pose a hazard to pets and children who may eat them.

Garter Snakes, genus *Thamnophis*

These are small to medium-sized snakes, usually with conspicuous light longitudinal stripes with a dark checkerboard pattern (produced by two rows of alternating dark squares on each side between the stripes). In some species and races the stripes are obscure and the checkerboard pattern very prominent. Most garter snakes have 17 to 21 rows of scales around the body (counted from the edge of the wide ventral or belly scales on one side, around the body in a diagonal straight line to the edge of the ventral scale on the other side). The centre (dorsal) stripe is always on the middle row of scales down the back, but the position of the side (lateral) stripe on each side is important in identifying some species. It may be positioned on the second, third or fourth row of scales (count up from the edge of the ventral scales).

Common Garter Snake
Couleuvre rayée
Thamnophis sirtalis
This species is the most variable, abundant and widespread snake in Canada. Its stripes are usually prominent (except in those found in the Maritime Provinces) and the lateral stripe is always on the second and third scale rows. These snakes are generally brown or black in ground colour, with yellow or brownish stripes. In the Prairie Provinces and most of British Columbia they have vertical red bars between the stripes, most prominent on the forward portion of the body. Around mid-body there are 19 scale rows. In southwestern Ontario (Pelee Island, Point Pelee and Long Point particularly) a melanistic, or black, phase commonly occurs. It is satiny black above and below with a white chin. It can be distinguished from the Black Rat Snake by its keeled scales (a sharp longitudinal ridge prominent on all but the lowest rows of dorsal scales). The Black Rat Snake has smooth (keel-less) scales and usually some indication

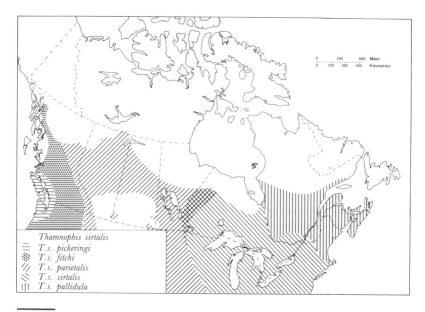

Thamnophis sirtalis
≡ T.s. *pickeringi*
⁞ T.s. *fitchi*
// T.s. *parietalis*
≋ T.s. *sirtalis*
||| T.s. *pallidula*

of the outlines of blotches. Some garter snakes in Nova Scotia also are melanistic or partly melanistic but are unlikely to be confused with any other species. Five races (subspecies) of the Common Garter Snake occur within Canada and are distinguished by colour and pattern. Maximum size is 124 cm.

Maritime Garter Snake
T. s. pallidula

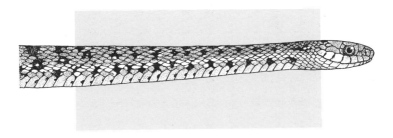

This subspecies is generally brown but varies from grey to cinnamon with a prominent checkerboard pattern of black or brown squares. The stripes are grey, brownish or yellowish, rarely orange. The lateral stripes are usually distinct but the dorsal are often obscure, only present on the forward part of the body, or absent altogether. It occurs through eastern Quebec, New Brunswick, Nova Scotia and Prince Edward Island.

Eastern Garter Snake
T. s. sirtalis

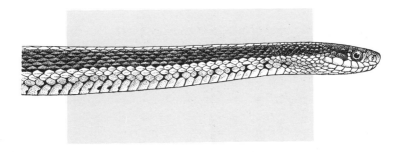

This is the most variable race in Canada. In some areas (particularly southwestern Quebec and southeastern Ontario) the ground colour is black with bright yellow stripes. In other areas the ground colour is lighter, most often brown, and the checker pattern between the stripes evident. The stripes may be greyish or brownish and in some areas either red or with red on the adjoining scales. The lateral stripe is on the second and third, never the fourth, row of scales. The Eastern Garter Snake ranges from western Quebec through Ontario to extreme eastern Manitoba.

Red-sided Garter Snake
T. s. parietalis

The ground colour of this race is black with prominent yellow stripes and red bars on the sides between the stripes. The red bars are usually not as prominent as in the Valley Garter Snake, and are best seen when the snake spreads its skin somewhat since much of the red is on the skin between the scales. It ranges from eastern Manitoba to eastern British Columbia and north of Fort Smith in the Northwest Territories. In the Prairie Provinces it is most widespread in the Boreal Forest. In the prairie region of southern Alberta and Saskatchewan it seems confined to areas of permanent water, such as river valleys, and is only locally abundant, being absent over much of the region.

Valley Garter Snake
T. s. fitchi

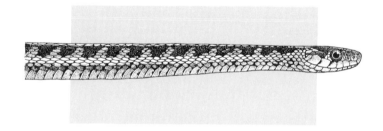

This race is black with yellow stripes like the Red-sided Garter Snake, but with more prominent red bars between the stripes, the red involving considerable portions of the scales as well as the skin between them. It has a prominent red suffusion on the side of the head (lacking in the Red-sided Garter Snake) and the top of the head is black (rather than olive as in the Red-sided). The dorsal stripe runs along the centre row and half of each adjacent row of scales. The Valley Garter Snake occurs over most of mainland British Columbia.

Puget Sound Red-sided Garter Snake
T. s. pickeringi

This subspecies is also a black garter snake with yellow stripes but its dorsal stripe is narrow, often only on the centre row of scales. The lateral stripe is bordered below by solid black, and the ventral surface is heavily marked with black, or is solid black, posteriorly. (The few ventral black markings of the Valley Garter Snake are usually confined to the tips of the ventral scales.) The red lateral blotches are variable. They may be small and mainly confined to the skin between the scales or large and conspicuous. This snake occurs on the southwestern mainland of British Columbia and on Vancouver Island.

All subspecies occupy a variety of terrestrial and aquatic edge habitats, overlapping the range and habitats of other members of the genus.

Eastern Ribbon Snake
Couleuvre mince
Thamnophis sauritus

Black ground colour, sharply defined yellow stripes and slender form characterize the Ribbon Snake. The yellow lips and dark of the remainder of the head are particularly sharply divided from each other in contrast to the Eastern Garter Snake *(T. sirtalis)* in which these colours are less distinct at their borders. The preocular scales (at the

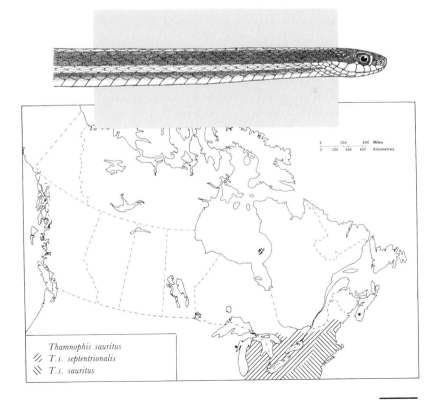

Thamnophis sauritus	
///	*T.s. septentrionalis*
\\\	*T.s. sauritus*

anterior edge of the eye) are always light coloured. The lateral stripe is on the third and fourth scale rows. The body is very slender compared to the Eastern Garter Snake, and the tail relatively much longer. Maximum size is 96.5 cm. The Canadian subspecies, the Northern Ribbon Snake, *T. s. septentrionalis*, occurs throughout much of southern Ontario and northern United States. A population in southwestern Nova Scotia is apparently a relict of a warmer period, now isolated from the main range of the species. It occupies margins of permanent water, particularly swamps, ponds and streams.

Butler's Garter Snake
Couleuvre à petite tête
Thamnophis butleri

Generally this snake is brown above, ranging from black to olive. A checkerboard pattern is not always evident. The stripes are generally yellowish but the lateral ones may be orange. The lateral stripe is centred on the third scale row anteriorly and extends to half of each of the fourth row above and the second row below; posteriorly

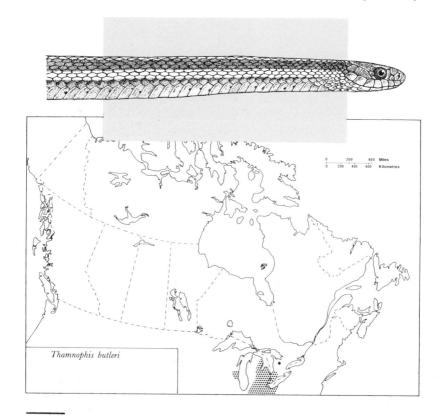

Thamnophis butleri

it may be only on the second and third rows. It does not exceed 69.2 cm in total length, and has a relatively small head. Butler's is recorded from a few localities in southwestern Ontario often in former prairie-like sometimes damp areas where it is often locally abundant.

Plains Garter Snake
Couleuvre des Plaines
Thamnophis radix

The ground colour of this robust snake is black to brown, with checkerboard pattern visible between stripes on brown individuals, obscured on black ones. The stripes are prominent; the lateral stripes are bright yellow and are located on scale rows three and four; the dorsal stripe is yellow in eastern Manitoba, orange or almost red in some of the Alberta specimens. The scale rows are usually 21 around midbody. It is relatively heavy-bodied for a garter snake, and reaches a maximum size of 178 cm. The Canadian subspecies, the Western Plains Garter Snake, *T. r. haydeni*, is widely distributed throughout the grassland and Aspen Parkland of Manitoba, Saskatchewan and Alberta, but does not invade coniferous forest. It frequents sloughs, marshes, streams and rivers.

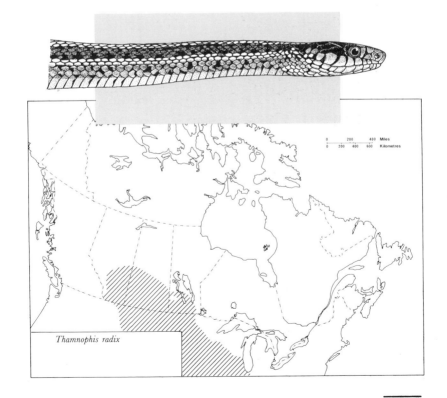

Thamnophis radix

Western Terrestrial Garter Snake
Couleuvre de l'Ouest
Thamnophis elegans

This snake is brown or grey, usually prominently checkered, although on the Pacific coast and Vancouver Island it may be almost black or sometimes blue. These bright to dull yellow stripes are present but the lateral ones are less prominent in specimens east of the Coast Range. The edges of the dorsal stripe tend to be wavy. The lateral stripe is on the second and third scale rows, and the scale rows at mid-body may be 21 or 19. Maximum length is 176 cm. It occurs widely over British Columbia and east across southern Alberta to central Saskatchewan. The subspecies found in Canada is the Wandering Garter Snake, *T. e. vagrans*. Despite the common name of the species this subspecies is as frequently found along the edge of aquatic habitats as it is in purely terrestrial ones. On the coasts of mainland British Columbia and Vancouver Island it often hunts tide pools for the fish left behind at low tide, and elsewhere in its range it commonly hunts stream and river pools in the dry season when the water is low and fish are concentrated in them. It also preys on small mammals.

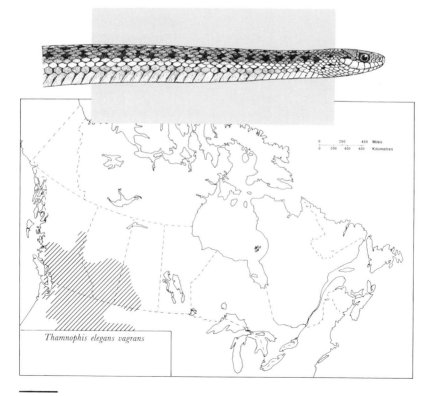

Thamnophis elegans vagrans

Northwestern Garter Snake
Couleuvre du Nord-Ouest
Thamnophis ordinoides

This small garter snake is extremely variable in colour. The ground colour may be black or brown to red, greenish or bluish with a dark checked pattern usually evident. The stripes may be distinct but can be faint or absent. The dorsal stripe varies from yellow to orange or red, the lateral stripes are greyish to greenish blue. The underside is greenish, bluish or reddish brown and may have bright red blotches. Melanistic (black) and albinistic (white) individuals are fairly common. The lateral stripe is on the second and third scale rows, and the dorsal rows are usually 17 at mid-body (thus distinguishing it from other western Canadian *Thamnophis*, which have 19 or 21 rows). It reaches a maximum length of 660 mm. It occurs in southern and western mainland British Columbia and Vancouver Island. Similar in habitat and feeding habits to the Redbelly and Brown Snakes (genus *Storeria*) of western Canada, it is found in thickets along roadsides and fields and rarely enters the water. It feeds primarily on slugs and earthworms.

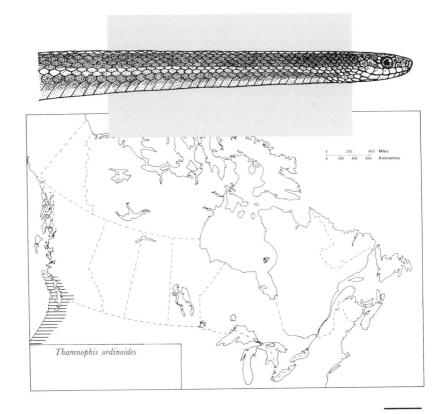

Thamnophis ordinoides

Water Snakes, genera *Nerodia* and *Regina*

Nerodia are generally stout, thick-bodied, largish, often blotched water snakes; *Regina* are more slender and smaller, often with a pattern of dark stripes.

Northern Water Snake
Couleuvre d'eau
Nerodia sipedon

This is a fairly large, stout, thick species with a wedge-shaped head. It attains a maximum length of 135 cm. Water snakes are sometimes mistaken for Cottonmouths ("water moccasins"), the venomous semiaquatic pit vipers of the southern United States. (The true Cottonmouth, genus *Agkistrodon*, does not occur north of southeastern Virginia and has a facial pit between eye and nostril, and large, hollow, paired fangs at the front of the upper jaw.) Water snakes are extremely vicious when cornered or first captured, but are not poisonous. Bacterial infections that cause local swelling may occur after bites, however. Two races occur in Canada.

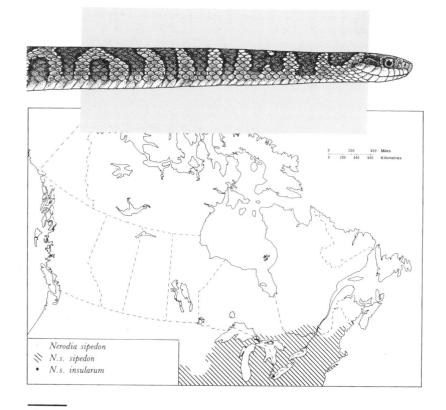

Nerodia sipedon
\\\ N.s. sipedon
• N.s. insularum

Northern Water Snake
N. s. sipedon

This banded snake is characterized by a dorsal series of dark brown squares with narrow, light cream to light brown bands separating them, and a lateral series of narrower dark squares with wide reddish bands between them. Through most of its length the dorsal and the lateral light bands are staggered in relation to each other, but on the forward part of some specimens they are joined, leaving the dorsal and lateral brown squares joined to form a continuous brown vertical bar. In large individuals the pattern is so faint they appear almost uniformly brown or black. The undersides of these snakes are yellowish to whitish, usually with rust coloured crescents on each ventral scale and black speckling, which may be quite heavy towards the tail.

This race occurs over southern Ontario and southern Quebec along river, stream, pond and lake margins. It is often seen along rocky shorelines where it basks on rocks, and takes cover under them. It is an agile and strong swimmer and readily takes to the water when disturbed, sometimes swimming with its head out and its body barely under the surface.

Lake Erie Water Snake
N. s. insularum

In coloration, the most extreme individuals of this race are uniformly grey above without any markings, but some banding may be evident along the back in some, and others show transitions toward the coloration of the typical subspecies, *N. s. sipedon*. The Lake Erie Water Snake is restricted to the Ohio and Ontario chain of islands of the western end of Lake Erie. In Ontario it is common on the rocky shores of Pelee Island and Middle Island. Although typically banded individuals, resembling *N. s. sipedon*, do also appear in these island populations, it has been suggested that they are more conspicuous on the rocky shores than the grey or partly grey individuals predominant in *N. s. insularum* populations, and are more readily seen and eaten, especially when very young, by bird predators such as gulls. These water snakes feed mainly on fish and frogs.

Queen Snake
Couleuvre royale
Regina septemvittata

This smaller, more slender water snake can grow to a maximum length of 92.1 cm but is generally not over 61 cm. It is rather nondescript brown above with a yellowish stripe along the side on the first and second scale rows, with three narrow dark stripes down the back. These stripes are barely visible if the ground colour is particularly

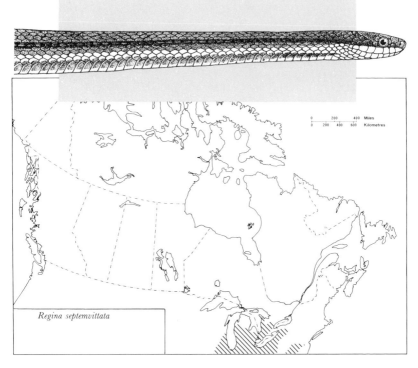

Regina septemvittata

dark. There are four longitudinal brown stripes on the yellow belly, plain and distinct on young individuals but tending to run together and to become generally more obscure on older adults.

In Canada this species is restricted to small rivers in the southwestern portion of Ontario. It is most often found by turning flat rocks along the water's edge. The Queen Snake feeds largely on crayfish, especially those that are still soft-shelled after moulting.

Small Harmless Snakes
The species grouped here are not all closely related but are described together because of their small size, and the similarity of colour patterns between some of them.

These are generally secretive snakes, rarely seen in the open, often most active at night. They are frequently found under logs, boards, stones (particularly flat ones), sheets of metal or tarpaper and similar cover. Some thrive close to human habitation, in vacant lots and parks in cities, and around garbage dumps. They are shy, inoffensive creatures, generally too small to bite humans, though one, the Redbelly Snake, will occasionally curl its upper lip to expose its minute teeth in an attempt at intimidation. They are either live-bearing *(Storeria)* or egg-laying *(Diadophis, Opheodrys, Contia, Hypsiglena)*, the *Contia* often in communal nests where several females deposit clutches together in a particularly suitable rotting log or under a large flat stone. Snake eggs are usually white, elongately oval, and tend to adhere to each other when first laid. Some egg-laying species (particularly the Smooth Green Snake) lay eggs fairly advanced in embryonic development, and the hatching time after laying may be relatively short.

Brown and Redbelly Snakes, genus *Storeria*

Two species in this genus occur in eastern Canada and can be distinguished most readily by belly colour and the number of dorsal scale rows around the body. These small-headed snakes are apparently primarily slug and earthworm feeders, and are sometimes extremely abundant in localized areas. They frequent clearings and bushy areas, and are most often found where there is an abundance of cover such as boards and logs and flat stones to offer them shelter. Clearings, pastures, old fields, abandoned farms and bush appear to be their typical habitat, but this may be because they are most easy to search for in such places. Both Brown and Redbelly snakes occur in southern Ontario and in southern Quebec but where one is abundant the other is generally rare or absent. In habitat and feeding activities they are remarkably similar to the small, small-headed *Thamnophis* of western North America, the Northwestern Garter Snake, *T. ordinoides*. No species of *Storeria* occur west of Saskatchewan in North America. The genus is thought to have been derived from *Nerodia-Thamnophis* stock.

In common with *Thamnophis*, *Nerodia* and *Regina*, species of *Storeria* have keeled scales (a raised longitudinal ridge along the middle of most dorsal scales), and divided anal scales.

Redbelly Snake
Couleuvre à ventre rouge
Storeria occipitomaculata

The maximum length of the Redbelly Snake is 40.6 cm. It is a brown, grey or black snake above, with a dark line on each side of the back and another along each side, although these may not be prominent. Rarely the mid-back area between the stripes is light (yellowish brown) and the sides are grey to almost black. There are three light, usually yellow, diamond-shaped spots on the neck, one on the centre and one on each side, which may be fused to appear as a neck ring, particularly in newborn young. The underside is bright red to rich "cream of tomato soup" orange. The chin and throat are white. It has 15 rows of

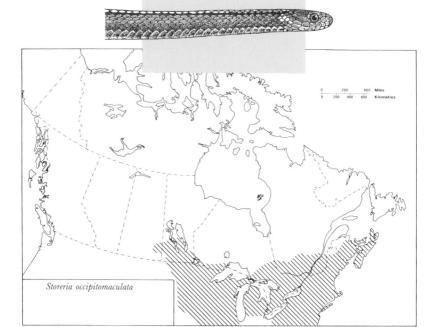

Storeria occipitomaculata

keeled dorsal scales. In Canada, the Redbelly Snake has a wide distribution from eastern Saskatchewan to Prince Edward Island. Its northern limit is yet undetermined but it is reported to reach the James Bay lowland in Ontario.

Brown Snake
Couleuvre brune
Storeria dekayi

The maximum length of this snake is 52.7 cm. It is brown in dorsal coloration but generally a paler brown than in the brown phase of the Redbelly Snake. There are two rows of dark spots down the back, and in some individuals these are connected, or partly connected, across the back by dark bars. The back, between the spots, is usually paler than the brown of the sides, giving a suggestion of a wide mid-dorsal stripe.

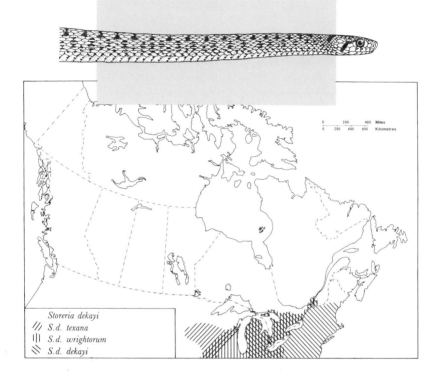

Storeria dekayi
/// S.d. texana
||| S.d. wrightorum
\\\ S.d. dekayi

There is a dark, diagonal line on the side of the head. The belly is light, generally nearly white to pink in coloration but may be somewhat yellowish or brownish. There are 17 rows of scales around the body. The young have a yellowish band around the neck, and the dark dorsal spots are not well developed.

In Canada the Brown Snake is much more restricted in distribution than the Redbelly, occurring only in southwestern Ontario, along the St. Lawrence River in eastern Ontario, and at a few localities in southern Quebec. The populations in southwestern Ontario are intergrades intermediate between the Northern Brown Snake, *S. d. dekayi*, which has dots without connecting cross bands on the back and in which the sum of ventral (belly) and subcaudal (underside of tail) scales total 175 or fewer, and the Midland Brown Snake, *S. d. wrightorum*, which has bars across the back and 176 or more ventral and subcaudal scales combined. Populations in Quebec may more closely resemble the Northern Brown Snake.

Other Small Snakes, genera *Diadophis,*
Opheodrys, Contia and *Hypsiglena*

These four probably unrelated colubrid genera always have smooth dorsal scales (never keeled). *Opheodrys* and *Diadophis* have uniform body coloration, *Contia* has faint dark longitudinal stripes, and *Hypsiglena* is spotted. The young of all other Canadian snakes can be distinguished by their smooth scales from the keeled, scaled young of the garter and water snakes *(Thamnophis, Nerodia, Regina)* and the Redbelly and Brown snakes *(Storeria)*. The young of the larger harmless snakes *(Lampropeltis, Heterodon, Coluber, Pituophis, Elaphe)* and the rattlesnakes *(Crotalus, Sistrurus)* all have a blotched pattern, and only *Hyporglena* can be confused with them. The latter, however, has a vertical eye pupil (round in the young of the larger harmless snakes) and lacks the button (initial rattle segment) of the vertical eye-pupiled young rattlesnakes.

Smooth Green Snake
Couleuvre verte
Opheodrys vernalis

This is thought by many to be the most strikingly beautiful snake in Canada. It is unmarked, bright satiny green above and white or yellowish white below. The young tend to be duller in coloration, olive to bluish grey. The maximum length of adults is 66 cm. In Canada the species ranges from Prince Edward Island to central Saskatchewan. Populations in eastern Canada belong to the Eastern Smooth Green Snake, *O. v. vernalis*, distinguished from the western race by having 130 or fewer ventral belly scales in the male and 139 or fewer in the female. The Western Smooth Green Snake, *O. v. blanchardi*, has 131 or more ventrals in the male and 140 or more in the female. Specimens from Manitoba and Saskatchewan are intermediate between the two subspecies and may be referred to as intergrades, *O. v. vernalis* × *blanchardi*. Pure populations of *O. v. blanchardi* occur south of central Canada.

This is a snake of grassy clearings, meadows and bushy areas, often where it is moist. It will climb low bushes readily. It is rarely seen in the open, probably because its colour blends so well with any green vegetation. On an area of bare ground such as an unpaved road

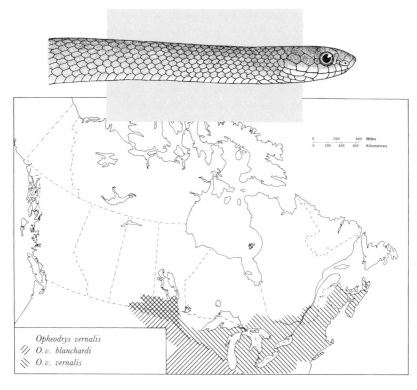

Opheodrys vernalis
/// O.v. blanchardi
\\\ O.v. vernalis

it stands out like a blade of fresh cut grass, and most individuals seen are in such situations or found under boards, rocks or similar cover. It feeds largely on spiders, caterpillars, grasshoppers, crickets and snails.

Ringneck Snake
Couleuvre à collier
Diadophis punctatus

A bluish or slate grey smooth body with a bright yellow neck ring identifies this snake. The belly is also yellow and may have black dots, either down the centre or, rarely, paired. Its maximum length is 62.5 cm. In Canada, the subspecies represented is the Northern Ringneck Snake, *D. p. edwardsi*. It occurs in southern Ontario and Quebec and in New Brunswick and Nova Scotia. This is an extremely secretive snake of woodlands, but may be locally abundant. It is found under flat rocks (particularly in areas of slate slabs), logs and similar cover and is rarely seen in the open. It may be most active at night. It feeds mostly on small salamanders, but frogs, earthworms and small snakes are also taken.

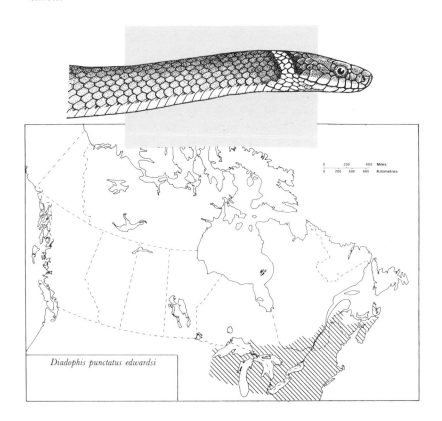

Diadophis punctatus edwardsi

Sharptail Snake
Couleuvre à queue fine
Contia tenuis

The coloration of the Sharptail Snake is brown above, ranging from reddish to grey with a tendency to be reddish on the tail. A faint yellowish or orange-red line is often present on each side of the body. The belly is marked alternately with dark brown or black and greyish or cream crossbars. The tip of the tail has a pointed spine. Its maximum length is 46 cm. In Canada, it has been recorded several times on North Pender Island and once on South Pender Island both near the southern end of Vancouver Island, and recently, on southern Vancouver Island itself. Two specimens have been collected in the southern interior mainland near Chase in the Fraser River Drainage. The 378 km gap between the records may be a tribute to the secretiveness of the species rather than an indication of a discontinuous distribution. It is found in grassland and forest, often near streams, and in suburban yards. It is rarely seen in the open, almost always being taken under rocks, logs and similar

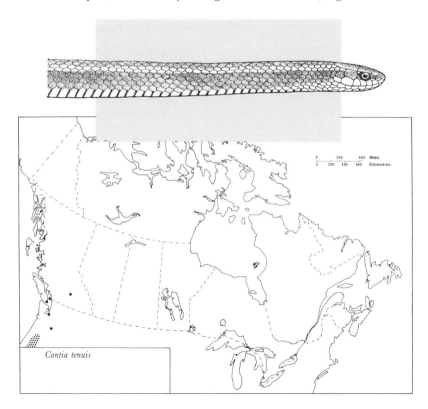

Contia tenuis

cover. Elsewhere in its range it has been reported to be extremely locally abundant. It is known to feed only on small slugs, and has enlarged teeth ideal for holding such mucous-covered prey.

Night Snake
Couleuvre nocturne
Hypsiglena torquata

This small and secretive snake was only added to the Canadian herpetofauna in 1980. It attains a maximum length of 66 cm and is grey to brownish with large dark grey or brown spots along the back and sides. Prominent blotches are present on the neck, and a stripe extends along the side of the head to the snout. The underside is white and unmarked except for fine speckling adjacent to the sides. The scales are smooth (unkeeled) and are in 21 rows at mid-body. It has vertical eye pupils, a characteristic that readily distinguishes it from all other blotched Canadian species except the rattlesnakes.

Hypsiglena torquata

The subspecies recorded in Canada is the Desert Night Snake, *H. t. deserticola*, collected in the lower Okanagan valley in south-central British Columbia.

As its name implies, the Night Snake is active after dark. It occurs in a variety of dry habitats from prairie to woodland over its range. It possesses a mild venom, which is injected through grooved, enlarged teeth at the rear of the upper jaws. Its prey are lizards, salamanders, frogs and toads. Although toxic to these animals, its bite is not believed to be dangerous to humans.

It lays eggs; recorded clutches for the subspecies are from four to six, but for the species as a whole clutches vary from three to 12.

Larger Harmless Snakes

Seven moderate-sized to very large colubrid snakes occur in Canada, including *Heterodon*, the Hognose Snakes, and *Elaphe*, the Rat Snakes, each with two species occurring in Canada; *Pituophis*, the Bullsnakes and Gopher Snakes with one species and three subspecies in Canada; *Coluber*, the Racers with one species and three subspecies in Canada; and *Lampropeltis*, the Milk Snakes, with a single species. These snakes range from 89.5 cm maximum length of the Western Hognose to the 256.5 cm of the Rat Snake.

The Hognose Snakes feed on toads and frogs; Racers eat a large variety of animals including amphibians, reptiles and insects as well as birds and mammals; and the *Elaphe*, *Pituophis* and *Lampropeltis* are primarily bird and mammal predators, though the Milk Snakes will also eat other snakes and lizards. These three genera often constrict their prey like boas, to suffocate it before eating.

Most of these large snakes are terrestrial, though the Fox Snake, *Elaphe vulpina*, frequents marshes probably to hunt aquatic and semi-aquatic birds and mammals. All but the Hognose Snakes will readily climb and hunt in bushes and trees. All have a blotched dorsal pattern, although the Eastern Hognose, *Heterodon platyrhinos*, has a black, or melanistic phase as well, and in the Racers, *Coluber*, and the Black Rat Snake, *Elaphe obsoleta*, the blotched pattern is present only on the young. Adults are completely or largely unicoloured above, with only faint traces of blotches, or no traces at all. The Hognose Snakes are thick-bodied, slow, specialized colubrids, but the other four genera are elongate, generalized, fairly active snakes. All lay eggs, and like some of the smaller colubrids, communal laying has been reported at least for the Rat Snake.

None of these larger harmless snakes penetrate very far north into Canada. None occur in the Maritime Provinces or on Vancouver Island, and only the Milk Snake is recorded for Quebec. Their centres of Canadian abundance are southwestern Ontario, the short-grass prairie of southwestern Saskatchewan and southeastern Alberta, and the warm, dry valleys of southern British Columbia.

Of all the harmless snakes in Canada, these species have suffered most from the invasion of European man. Not only has their habitat been greatly altered by farming and urban development (particulary in southwestern Ontario) but their size and activity (all but the Milk Snake are often conspicuously abroad in the daytime) have made them vulnerable to those dedicated people who firmly believe that "the only good snake is a dead snake" or who confuse their blotched patterns with those of poisonous snakes. All *can* bite, however, and frequently will, in defending themselves. Often they will try to escape detection by remaining motionless, trusting that they haven't been seen, but Racers, which are quick and nervous snakes, on some occasions act aggressively. Many large snakes will vibrate their tails when they are nervous; in dry leaves, or other dead vegetation, this can produce a whirring sound sometimes mistaken for the buzz of a rattlesnake, giving rise to one folk name for the Fox Snake, the "Hardwoods Rattler." The Bullsnake will expel air in a resounding hiss when particularly defensive.

Hognose Snakes, genus *Heterodon*
These are relatively squat, heavy-bodied snakes. Usually they have a dorsal pattern of blotches, though some individuals of the eastern species may be all black. They have flattened heads, keeled scales and modified nose scales, which give the snout an up-turned, hog-like, appearance, most pronounced in the western species. They prefer sandy areas, and feed largely on toads. Enlarged teeth allow these snakes to puncture the skin of a toad to deflate it after the toad has puffed up with air to make itself larger and more difficult to swallow.

The ability of Hognose Snakes to flatten their necks is reminiscent of the hood of a cobra. They will rear, flatten, hiss loudly, and occasionally even strike. This has earned them the folk name of "Puff-Adder," a name correctly applied only to a highly venomous true viper of Africa. The display of the Hognose is pure bluff, since the snake is without poison. In addition, many have observed that when it does strike it is always with the mouth closed! It rarely attempts to bite even when handled. However well its defensive stand and bluffing to frighten possible enemies may have served it in the past, it is usually fatal when tried on modern man. People are often thoroughly taken in by the display and bludgeon the actor to death. Hognose Snakes are now considered rare over most of their Canadian distribution.

If unmolested, but still faced with danger, the Hognose will often try a different tactic and go into simulated death throes, then lie limp, belly up. This ruse can be unmasked by turning the Hognose over—it generally will flip belly up again to show that it is really a dead snake and of no further interest to its tormentor. If the observer retreats but watches from a distance, the snake will soon right itself and quickly slip away. This death-feigning behaviour is seldom given by captive specimens. Hognose Snakes are restricted to North America.

Eastern Hognose Snake
Couleuvre à nez plat
Heterodon platyrhinos

The maximum total length of this Hognose is 116 cm. It usually has a series of large black blotches down the back and smaller ones alternating on the sides. The colour is variable and may be blue, grey, yellowish or reddish. Occasional individuals are all black or all grey. The belly is whitish or yellowish with grey or brown mottling. The light-coloured underside of the tail lacks this mottling, which ends abruptly at the anal scale. The slightly upturned nose is the best identifying

Heterodon platyrhinos

mark. In Canada it is restricted to southern Ontario, ranging as far north as the southern boundary of Algonquin Provincial Park. In some areas of its former range it appears to have completely disappeared.

Western Hognose Snake
Couleuvre à nez retroussé
Heterodon nasicus

The maximum total length of the Western Hognose is 89.5 cm. A dorsal row of dark blotches and an alternating row on each side mark this generally light brown snake. The underside is whitish or yellowish with an irregular jet black central area. The underside of the tail is also heavily marked with black, in contrast to the light underside of the tail in the eastern species. The nose tip is strongly upturned. In Canada it occurs in the short-grass prairie of southern Saskatchewan and Alberta and in the sandy deposits in southwestern Manitoba. Since it is rarely seen, its real abundance is difficult to assess, but it apparently is not common anywhere within this range.

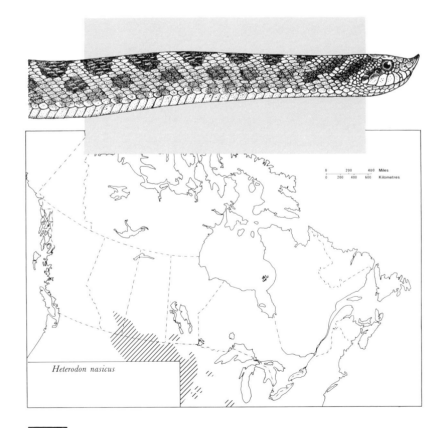

Heterodon nasicus

Rat Snakes, genus *Elaphe*

These are large colubrids, some attaining lengths of over 200 cm. They tend to be flattened beneath, with the sides and the belly meeting at a sharp angle, giving them a cross-section likened to a loaf of bread by some herpetologists. Often the scales along the back have low, weak keels, but the first three to five scale rows of the sides are smooth. The genus is widespread and ranges over North and Central America, Europe and Asia. Newly hatched Rat Snakes have a pattern or dorsal blotches and alternating lateral spots, but these are lost or obscured in adults of some species.

Rat Snake
Couleuvre obscure
Elaphe obsoleta

The maximum recorded length of this Rat Snake is 256.5 cm and individual specimens of more than 152 cm are not uncommon in Canada. The adults (107 cm and over) are black above, but sometimes the traces of the blotched pattern of the young will be evident, out-

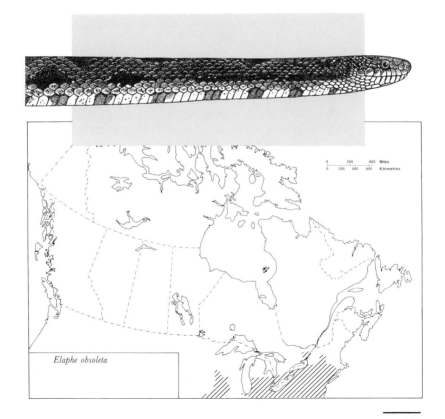

Elaphe obsoleta

lined by traces of pale yellowish or reddish on the skin between the scales. The throat is white; the belly is white to yellowish anteriorly and usually has squarish dark markings. Posteriorly, the underside becomes mottled with black, which obscures this pattern. In Canada this snake is confined to two apparently disjunct areas in southern Ontario. In the southwestern portion it is becoming rare or absent in most of the formerly occupied region, though it may still be locally abundant in a few areas. In central Ontario it is still common in the Rideau Lakes region, where the generally rocky terrain has been relatively unsuited to intensive agriculture. However, with increasing development of tourism in this region, more people intolerant of snakes, especially large snakes, are visiting or settling the area. As with other large snakes, the temptation to bask on sun-heated asphalt highways often proves fatal as well.

The Rat Snake is an excellent and frequent climber, and generally inhabits woodlands and uplands away from water, for which reason it has been called the Highland Black Snake. Another name is Pilot Black Snake, given to it in the United States where it occupies the same areas as rattlesnakes and may den in the same sites. According to folklore it guides the rattlesnakes to these dens in the fall.

Fox Snake
Couleuvre fauve
Elaphe vulpina

The maximum recorded length of the Fox Snake is 174 cm. Prominent dorsal blotches of dark brown alternate with two series of smaller lateral blotches or spots of brown or black. The ground colour is generally yellowish brown. The young have a prominent cross-band on the head but in larger individuals this fades to leave a generally brown head, which retains only scattered flecks of dark pigment. The belly is yellow with squarish dark blotches that continue along the underside of the tail.

Young Fox Snakes might be confused with the blotched young Racers, Rat Snakes or especially Milk Snakes, all of which overlap their range. Racers and Milk Snakes, however, have entirely smooth scales, and Rat Snakes have weak keels on the dorsal scales although these may not be developed in newly hatched individuals. Young Racers have little or no pattern on the tail, young Rat Snakes have prominent blotches; Milk Snakes have an undivided anal scale (in front of vent), Rat Snakes have a divided anal scale. A count of the belly (ventral) scales will separate the Rat Snake and the Fox Snake: Fox Snakes have 216 or fewer ventrals, Rat Snakes have 221 or more.

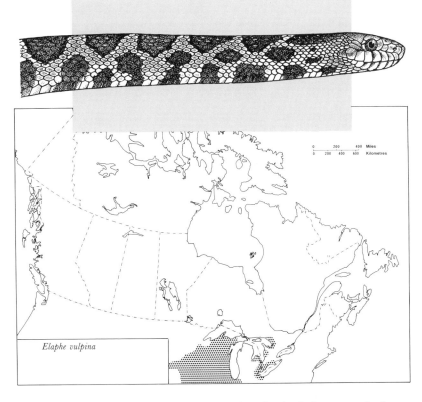

Elaphe vulpina

In Canada the Fox Snake is known only from the marshlands and adjacent areas of southwestern Ontario, particularly the marshes of Lake Erie, Lake Huron and Georgian Bay. The subspecies in Canada is the Eastern Fox Snake, *E. v. glodyi*. It is generally found near or in water. Its coloration has occasionally led some observers to mistake it for the Copperhead *(Agkistrodon contortrix)*, a blotched poisonous pit viper of the eastern United States. The true Copperhead has crossbands in an hourglass pattern, wide at the sides and narrow at the midpoint of the back. It does not occur north of Massachusetts and central Illinois.

Gopher Snake
Couleuvre à nez mince
Pituophis melanoleucus

The maximum recorded length of the Gopher Snake is 254 cm. The head is relatively small for the body size and flattened somewhat along the sides giving it a more pointed outline than other Canadian snakes. This may help it to see forward in mammal burrows

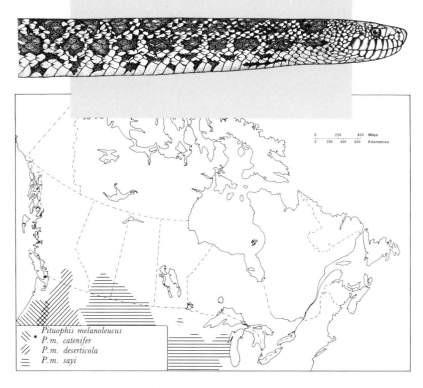

Pituophis melanoleucus
• P.m. catenifer
P.m. deserticola
P.m. sayi

when hunting, or in burrowing for itself. The rostral scale on the nose is enlarged but barely raised above the adjacent head scales. These snakes are generally yellowish to creamish coloured with prominent dorsal blotches of black, brown and reddish brown with smaller darker blotches on the sides. The blotches on the sides of the neck sometimes fuse into a longitudinal stripe. The pattern is most distinct on the forward part of the body. The underside is white to yellowish with black blotches.

Three subspecies have been recorded for Canada. The Bullsnake, *P. m. sayi*, which occurs in the short-grass prairie of southern Alberta and Saskatchewan, has a narrower, much higher than wide, scale on the nose (the rostral scale), which is raised above the adjacent head scales. The Gopher Snakes occur in British Columbia. The Great Basin Gopher Snake, *P. m. deserticola*, occurs in the arid valleys and wooded slopes throughout southern British Columbia. The lateral blotches on the sides of the neck commonly fuse to form a longitudinal band in this subspecies. The Pacific Gopher Snake, *P. m. catenifer*, has been reported recently only once from the coastal island of Galiano and, in the previous century, from the mainland at Sumas just south of the British Columbia border. It typically has a greyish suffusion on the sides of the body and underside of the tail. The presence of natural populations of this race in British Columbia needs further confirmation.

These can be aggressive snakes in the wild, coiling, hissing explosively, like the angry snort of a bull, and striking out in defence. However, they are more commonly mild and retiring. They often den in the same sites with rattlesnakes. Folklore that they kill rattlesnakes is exaggerated; they are mainly mammal predators. Another tale of the prairies concerns the mythical Bullrattler, a supposed hybrid from a Bullsnake-rattlesnake cross, which is reputed to produce a snake larger and more venomous than the rattlesnake, and lacking its warning rattle. This legendary beast may be inspired in part by the occasional Bullsnake that coils, vibrates its tail (in common with many large harmless snakes) and freely strikes out, an awe-inspiring sight when enacted by a snake 2 m or more in length. It is the type of story relished in the telling by old hands of prairie life, fabricated to sort out the potential settler from the transient visitor among the listening newcomers, and part of the ancient parlour game of turn-about telling of tales of ever decreasing credibility until one is reached that even the most gullible of the audience will not believe.

The genus *Pituophis* contains only this single species and is restricted to North America. The subspecies occurring in the southeastern United States is called the Pine Snake; these and the Canadian subspecies, the Bullsnake and the Gopher Snakes, were once regarded as distinct species.

Milk Snake
Couleuvre tachetée
Lampropeltis triangulum

A maximum length of 132 cm has been recorded for this species, but a 91 cm individual is considered large in Canada. A prominent series of brown, black-bordered, dorsal blotches and two series of alternating lateral blotches are present on a light grey to creamish tan colour. In young Milk Snakes the dorsal blotches are bright reddish brown and the ground colour is very pale. The blotch on the back of the neck is characteristically Y or V shaped. The underside is white, marked with a more-or-less checkerboard pattern of black. All scales are smooth; the anal scale is undivided.

In Canada, Milk Snakes occur in southern Ontario and Quebec. They are generally secretive, though they may occasionally hunt in barns and other outbuildings for mice and small rats. Their presence in stables formerly gave rise to the myth that they actually sucked

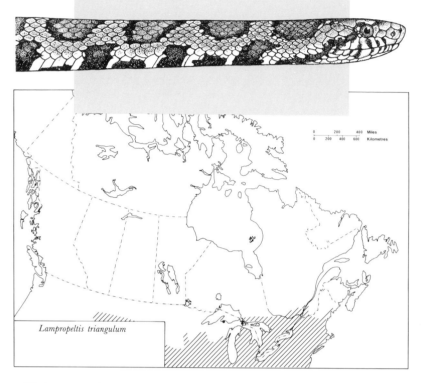

Lampropeltis triangulum

milk from cows' udders. The needle-sharp teeth of a Milk Snake should have been enough to dispel any credibility in the tale, or a calculation of its stomach volume enough to discredit the amount it was supposed to extract. (Farmers actually blamed the snake for a fall in milk production in their cattle.) However, the desire to have some excuse for killing snakes on sight was usually sufficient to override reason, and the common name became firmly attached to this reptile, whose presence in barns and stables is actually beneficial since it controls the rodent population.

The same species in the southern United States has races with a banded, instead of blotched, pattern. These, and related species, are called Kingsnakes because of their predation on snakes of other species. The genus *Lampropeltis* is restricted to North, Central and northern South America.

Racer
Couleuvre agile
Coluber constrictor

The maximum recorded length is 182.9 cm for the Blue Racer. The Eastern Yellow-belly Racer attains nearly this length but the western race is smaller. They are slender, smooth-scaled snakes with a divided anal scale. The young have dorsal blotches at hatching but are patternless by maturity. Three races are recorded in Canada. The Blue Racer, *C. c. foxi*, formerly occurred in portions of extreme southwestern Ontario but now is only known with certainty on Pelee Island where it is protected by a reserve and strict prohibition against killing, capture, or habitat destruction, by Ontario's Endangered Species Act. It is blue above, sometimes greenish or greyish blue. The chin and the throat are white and the belly is pale bluish. The Eastern Yellow-belly Racer, *C. c. flaviventris*, is known only from two areas of extreme southern Saskatchewan in the Frenchman and Big Muddy valleys. It is generally brownish above but grey, olive and even dull blue variations have been

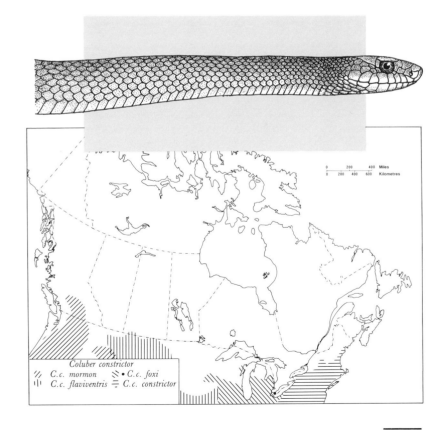

	Coluber constrictor	
//	C.c. mormon	• C.c. foxi
|||	C.c. flaviventris	≡ C.c. constrictor

noted. The belly is yellow. The Western Yellow-belly Racer, *C. c. mormon*, is widespread and common in portions of southern British Columbia. It is grey-brown or olive above, pale yellow below, and is distinguished from the eastern race by usually having eight scales along the upper lip (supralabial scales) and more than 85 paired scales under the tail (subcaudals). The eastern race usually has seven supralabials and less than 85 subcaudals.

Canadian Racers seem to prefer open areas, especially grassland and light bush-covered areas. Racers will readily climb bushes and lower branches of trees. They feed on frogs, lizards, insects, rodents and small birds. Despite the scientific name *constrictor*, applied in an early wave of describing animals from pickled specimens when the creature had not been observed alive by the describer, this snake does *not* constrict its prey. It may throw a loop over a victim and press it down to subdue struggling, however. Racers range through North America to Central America, and other species occur in Europe, Northern Africa and Asia.

Family Viperidae
Vipers

There are two main groupings of poisonous or venomous snakes in the world: the Viperidae, which includes the Old World vipers and the pit vipers (sometimes recognized as a separate family, the Crotalidae); and the Elapidae (coral snakes, cobras and their close relative: mambas, kraits and others) and Hydrophidae (the sea-snakes). Some authorities split the Hydrophidae, separating the family Laticaudidae the sea kraits; others place all sea snakes into the Elapidae. Some members of the primarily harmless snake family Colubridae, which contains two-thirds of the world's snake fauna, are venomous, but these are generally tropical in distribution. No Canadian colubrid snake is venomous. None of the eleven other families of snakes in the world has poisonous members.

Of the families in which all species have poison-producing glands and efficient means of injecting it, the Elapidae contain the most dangerous snakes. Both viperids and elapids have enlarged paired front fangs in the upper jaw. Those in Elapidae are shorter, fixed in position, contain a canal and usually have a trace of a posterior groove. In the Viperidae the fangs are on a moveable bone and fold against the roof of the mouth when the mouth is closed. Viperid fangs have a central canal and lack any trace of a posterior groove. They resemble curved hypodermic needles. When striking, snakes of this family erect the fangs and tend to strike forward, directly toward their victim or tormentor with a stabbing thrust; the head is usually immediately drawn back after contact. Elapids tend to strike downward and to hold on. They are not able to inject quantities of venom as quickly and efficiently as viperids. The duct of the poison gland in elapids empties into a gum cavity above the fang canal on each side. In viperids the gland duct is connected directly to the tooth canal.

Although a variety of effects are produced by the venom of these snakes, that of elapids is primarily neurotoxic (acting on the nervous system) and that of viperids is primarily hemotoxic (acting on the blood). Neurotoxins kill effectively and often quickly by paralyzing the respiratory system, thus suffocating the victim, whereas hemotoxins break down red blood cells and cause extensive internal hemorrhaging. The potency of the venom varies with the species. The size of the snake governs both the amount of poison it will have available to inject and the size of the fangs for inflicting a bite. Furthermore, the amount of poison varies with the time lapsed since the last use and the general health of the snake. Of the two groups, elapids grow to a larger size; the King Cobra *(Ophiophagus hannah)* may exceed 540 cm in length. The largest viperid is the tropical American Bushmaster, *Lachesis muta*, which attains nearly 360 cm in length.

The only terrestrial elapids of the American continent are the coral snakes *(Micrurus* and *Micruroides)* of southern North America, Central and South America. In the Old World, elapids are very abundant in the tropical and subtropical regions, outnumbering all other families of snakes in Australia. This family includes cobras, some of which "spit" venom into the eyes of enemies, as well as a wide variety of forms that defend themselves more conventionally.

The viperids are well represented in both New and Old Worlds, and are tolerant of cool climates. The Common Adder of Europe *(Vipera berus)* ranges to over 2376 m in the Alps and to the Arctic Circle in Scandinavia and Finland. In North America, rattlesnakes (genera *Crotalus* and *Sistrurus*) are the most northerly although *Crotalus* only reaches southern British Columbia, Alberta, Saskatchewan and Ontario, and *Sistrurus* is found in southern Ontario. The harmless garter snakes *(Thamnophis)* are the most northerly snakes in North America, in contrast to Europe where their relative, the Grass Snake *(Natrix natrix)*, falls just short of *Vipera* in northern distribution.

Viperids are divided among three subfamilies: the mole vipers (Atractaspidinae), the true vipers (Viperinae) and the pit vipers (Crotalinae). There is only one genus of mole viper, and approximately a dozen species, which occur in Africa, the Sinai Peninsula and the adjacent middle east. Viperidae consists of nine genera occurring only in Europe, Asia and Africa.

The Crotalinae differ from other vipers in possessing a pit on each side of the head between the eye and the nostril. This area is heat-sensitive and can detect small differences in temperature, alerting the snake to the exact location of warm-blooded animals. Apparently both direction and distance can be determined from this sensor, as pit vipers can strike prey accurately in the dark. The rattlesnakes *(Crotalus* and *Sistrurus)* are restricted to the Americas but other genera of pit vipers occur in eastern Europe, Asia, Japan and the Indo-Australian archipelago. Included with the rattlesnakes in this subfamily are the Cottonmouth and the Copperhead of eastern North America *(Agkistrodon)* and the Bushmaster *(Lachesis)* and Fer-de-Lance *(Bothrops)* of tropical America.

Pit vipers feed largely on birds and mammals. Often they will strike and withdraw, allowing their efficiently injected poison to kill their prey before they attempt to swallow it. If the victim has managed to move away before collapsing, then it is trailed by scent until found. These tactics probably allow the snake to subdue several prey in succession before eating, an advantage if a number of small rodents are found together. The pause before attempting to swallow the prey also reduces the chances of getting bitten by the sharp incisor teeth of rodent prey.

There are three strategies, then, carried out by snakes to deal with active mammal prey whose teeth and claws are capable of wounding, or even killing, their predators. The simplest, used by such generalized snakes as the garter snakes *(Thamnophis)*, is simply to swallow the prey head-first as quickly as possible, trusting that it will be too frightened to do any damage and that it will quickly suffocate within the snake. These snakes prey mainly on invertebrates, fish and amphibians and take other reptiles and mammals only occasionally, when the snake itself has reached a large size. The second method is to constrict the prey in coils of the body, quickly suffocating it by squeezing the lungs and probably also putting pressure on the heart to retard its beating and thus impede the circulation of blood. The third, which reaches its perfection in vipers, is to inject poison and retreat, reapproaching the meal only after it is totally incapacitated. The poison not only kills but also initiates digestion by starting tissue breakdown before the prey is even swallowed. This may have been its initial value in earlier snakes, before the shift to toxicity values evolved.

The usefulness of poison as a protection against animals that are not potential meals but which might themselves prey upon snakes has probably been a secondary, though important, advantage. When threatened, many snakes, particularly large ones, vibrate their tails whether or not they have poison, and in suitable surroundings (i.e. dry leaves) the rattling sound acts as an effective warning. Only the rattlesnakes produce a sound independent of their surroundings, with the rattle, a series of horny, loosely interlocking segments on their tail tips.

Snakebite causes many deaths per year in the world, particularly in tropical areas where people commonly go barefoot, where poisonous species are common, and where treatment may be difficult to obtain. Research has produced effective antidotes (antivenins) for snake poisoning which counteract its effects. In Canada these are readily available to medical authorities throughout the limited areas where our few poisonous species occur. In addition, the only poisonous species in Canada are rattlesnakes, and the action of their poisons, though exceedingly painful and accompanied by hemorrhaging, local swelling and tissue destruction, is usually relatively slow-acting. Unless one is in an extremely remote area, there is generally ample time to get to a regional hospital and receive expert treatment. The single most important field treatment for rattlesnake-bite is to keep the victim calm and as inactive as possible. He or she should be carried to the nearest vehicle and taken as quickly as possible to the nearest hospital. An over-excited nervous reaction and movement increase circulation, and therefore increase the speed of the dispersion of poison through the body. Alcohol, an ancient treatment, also increases circulation rate, and it and all other stimulants should be absolutely avoided. If possible bring the snake for positive identification.

Occasionally, people are so frightened after being bitten by a snake that they will actually develop symptoms of poisoning from the bite of a harmless species. Some people have a toxic reaction to the antivenin itself, so it should be administered only by a doctor and preferably only in cases where it is certain that the snake was poisonous and did actually bite. Some of the recommended field first-aid treatments such as incision of the wound through the fang punctures, suction to remove poison, and application of a tourniquet must be used with caution. The effects of these procedures can be many times more damaging than the bite. Careless incision can result in permanent damage and a high probability of infection. Tourniquets, improperly applied, or used for too long a time, can impede circulation too successfully. If suction is applied by mouth, the poison so removed can enter the circulation via any cut or open sore in the mouth, though rattlesnake venom is apparently harmless if swallowed (unless the swallower has ulcers).

Anyone on foot in a rattlesnake-inhabited area should be able to avoid being bitten by using the simplest of precautions. Always look where you step and do not reach into any crevice or under a log, without first looking carefully. Be a bit noisy when walking, not talkative but making noise by walking, since snakes don't usually respond to airborn sounds but are very sensitive to vibrations. Given advance warning, any snake, including a rattlesnake, will usually try to avoid contact with humans, or at least give them a buzzing warning of their own location. Sometimes, however, they will simply freeze and hope not to be noticed. Incidents of snakebite are rare in Canada, and few deaths ever occur. When people have been bitten it is usually because they have been careless and either stepped on a snake or tried to pick one up, either not knowing it was poisonous or else handling it carelessly. Held *directly* behind the head, a snake cannot bite.

Anyone really apprehensive of the dangers, and seeking to be well prepared for any emergency in rattlesnake areas, should determine in advance the location of the nearest hospital with antivenin and talk to a local doctor about the treatment he would recommend.

Most rattlesnakes can be instantly recognized by the horny interlocking segments on the tail tip. Newborn rattlers have only one blunt "button," or knob, and occasionally an older individual will have had its rattles broken off. A new segment is added each time the skin is shed, several times a year. Rattlesnakes are triangular-headed (in outline from above) heavy-bodied snakes with keeled scales and an undivided anal scale.

Pigmy Rattlesnakes, genus *Sistrurus*
These small rattlesnakes have nine large scales on the top of the head, a feature they have in common with harmless snakes.

Massasauga
Massasauga
Sistrurus catenatus
The maximum record length for the Massasauga is 100 cm but most individuals are smaller, rarely over 76 cm. There is a row of large dark blotches, brownish or black, down the back, and smaller blotches in three alternating rows along the sides. The ground colour between the blotches is grey. The underside is black, usually with some irregular markings of yellowish or white.

In Canada, the Massasauga is recorded from southwestern Ontario, along Lake Erie as far east as Hamilton, and north to Georgian Bay. In the latter area it has not been found east of the Muskoka Lakes. Throughout this range its numbers seem to be declining. It is rare or exterminated from most of the Lake Erie area although a small population still occurs in the Wainfleet marshes near Welland on the Niagara Peninsula. In the Georgian Bay area it may yet be abundant in some localities, but the increase in reports in the 1960s was likely due to an increase of cottages and tourists within the region, not an actual increase in the population of snakes. It is largely a lowland snake of marshy regions

Sistrurus catenatus

but it will hunt in adjacent uplands. Its hibernation sites in Ontario are unknown. It feeds primarily on frogs and rodents and will occasionally eat other snakes. It rarely attempts to bite, but its poison is quite toxic.

Common Rattlesnakes, genus *Crotalus*
This group is distinguished from the Pigmy Rattlesnakes *(Sistrurus)* by the small instead of large scales on the top of the head.

Timber Rattlesnake
Crotale des bois
Crotalus horridus
This large rattler's maximum recorded length is 189 cm. The body is banded with black or dark brown on a generally yellow ground colour (also brown or grey). The bands are widest in the centre of the back, and their edges slant backward. On the forward part of the

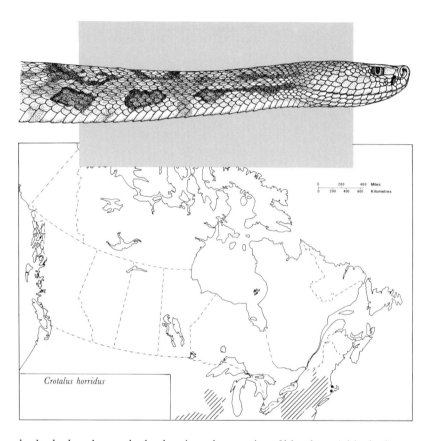

Crotalus horridus

body the bands may be broken into three series of blotches. A black phase has also been recorded in which the lighter ground colour is obscured by black stippling. The underside is yellowish with black mottling.

In Canada this rattlesnake occurred only in southwestern Ontario, and probably only within a summer's travel of rocky outcroppings where it could find suitable winter dens. The last specimen taken in Ontario was from Niagara Glen in 1941. Reports persist from Fitzwilliam Island in Georgian Bay of two kinds of rattlesnakes but these have never been confirmed, and are most likely based on colour variations of the Massasauga whose presence is verified on the island. The Timber Rattlesnake is now protected by the Ontario Endangered Species Act, in case a persisting population is discovered. This is a snake of wooded areas, and feeds mainly on rodents.

Western Rattlesnake
Crotale de l'Ouest
Crotalus viridis

The maximum recorded length for this species is 145 cm, but 114 cm is a large one. Western Rattlesnakes are marked with a pattern of large dark dorsal blotches and smaller lateral ones. Colour

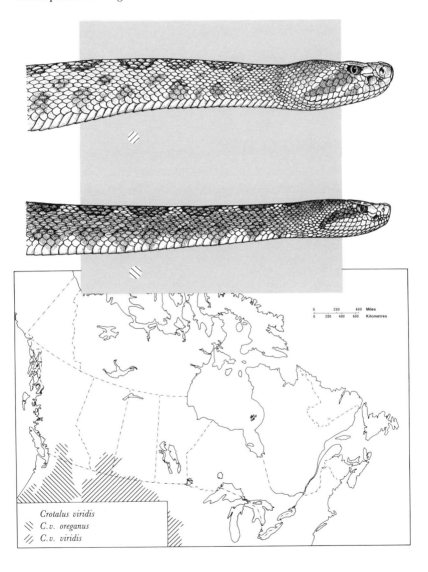

Crotalus viridis
\\\ *C.v. oreganus*
/// *C.v. viridis*

differences distinguish the races but even within one area there is often much variation, leading some people to believe more than one kind is present. Two races are found in Canada: the Prairie Rattlesnake, *C. v. viridis*, is usually light brown or yellowish, but may be somewhat greenish or greyish in ground colour with darker, but often not strongly contrasted, blotches. It occurs in southwestern Saskatchewan and southeastern Alberta in the arid short-grass prairie. Its range appears limited by the availability of river valley slopes, which afford suitable hibernating den sites, although it will move out some distance from these sites in summer.

The Northern Pacific Rattlesnake, *C. v. oreganus*, is darker than the prairie race with brown or black blotches and a cream to grey ground colour. It occurs in the arid valleys and their slopes in southern British Columbia.

Both races are primarily rodent eaters, and therefore beneficial where rodent control is desirable. They often den in fairly large numbers, and in the spring and fall are most often encountered near dens when they bask in the first or last heat of the year. It is at this time that they are most vulnerable to people bent on rattlesnake extermination. In some areas dens are systematically visited and all rattlesnakes in the open are slaughtered. Occasionally dynamite has been used to attempt to expose hibernating rattlesnakes. Despite vendettas of this type the species seems to be holding its own. Much of its distribution is in sparsely settled areas where it does not pose a great hazard to humans, though ranchers often feel it is an unnecessary hazard for range stock.

Field Study: Surveys and Conservation

Some groups of animals, insects and plants such as birds, butterflies and orchids, have great public appeal. Many noteworthy contributions to their study have been made by amateurs (the term is here used in the sense of anyone who conducts a study for the pure interest of it alone, rather than for financial gain). Such contributions are more rarely made in the study of amphibians and reptiles. In Canada, there are few herpetologists, scattered widely in a few museums and universities. The geographic area of the country is so vast that the task of studying local conditions, including abundance and population fluctuations, is immense.

As the southern portions of Canada, the very areas that contain the greatest diversity of amphibians and reptiles, become increasingly urbanized and more intensively farmed, suitable habitat for many species is shrinking. Knowledge of the exact distribution of each of these becomes essential if we are to save even some fragments of Canadian populations. Knowledge of the essential factors of temperature, moisture, and other aspects of habitat that contribute to the survival and reproduction of these species must be gathered in order to maintain their continued existence.

Any interested naturalist has an opportunity to make a useful contribution to our knowledge through detailed observations of local habitats of year-to-year variations in emergence, egg-laying, hatching, transformation, and of hibernation sites and duration for all species. Even occasional observations are of potential value. If careful records are made, and if copies are submitted to a central file, such as that maintained by the National Museum of Natural Sciences, they can be compared with the records of other observers; trends and patterns of ultimate scientific value could become evident.

The primary question is always: what species occur in the area? followed by why does it occur there and how does it survive. We still do not know the "what" for many areas in Canada. The "why" and "how" have been even less well studied. Many amphibians and reptiles are extremely secretive, and searching for them is only rewarding at certain times of the year, in certain restricted habitats, and under certain weather conditions. Other species are wide-ranging and are active and obvious under a wide variety of seasons and weather.

Frogs are the easiest of the native species of Canada on which to conduct a thorough survey. From the first warm weather of spring, as soon as most of the snow has melted, through to early summer, a succession of species gather at breeding sites and usually call

Species _____ No.____ | NMNS Cat. No.

Station No. ☐☐☐☐☐☐☐☐☐ | Accession No.
Field No. ☐☐☐☐☐☐ to ☐☐☐☐☐☐

Observations only△, Mark-release△, Ident.by _____

Locality _____

County/Dist. _____Province _____ Country_____

Date ☐☐ ☐☐☐☐ ☐☐☐ | Time(start) ☐☐☐ | dawn△ day △
| Time(finish) ☐☐☐ | dusk△ night△

Collector(s) _____

Weather _____

Habitat(vegetation/water type/human impact/temp/topography)
_____
_____
_____

Capture data _____

Other species(observed △ , captured△)_____
_____

Remarks and measurements
_____
_____
_____
_____
_____
_____
_____
_____
_____
_____
_____
_____

National Museum of Natural Sciences; Herpetology Section
Ottawa, Ontario K1A 0M8 c/o Dr. F.R. Cook

Sample of Field Observation Card for amphibian and reptile studies. These cards for submitting information for the scientific files of the National Museum of Natural Sciences are available from the Herpetology Section.

loudly. All Canadian species that call do so from water, or from grass clumps, bushes or trees in or bordering water. Each kind has its own distinctive call, and with a little patience and luck a call can be traced to its originator, and the species identified. Rubber boots, or even hip or chest waders, are invaluable in searching frog breeding sites.

Just after dark is always the best time for such searches, with a head-lamp or a flashlight. Some frogs will call during daylight, but are generally too shy to be approached at this time. After dark they are most vocal, and can be easily approached with an artificial light if care is taken not to splash or make a noise. If the night is warm, and particularly if breeding is at its peak, many species will continue to call under bright artificial light as vigorously as if it was still dark around them. The hour immediately after dark is best because as the evening cools, especially on clear nights, calling loses its vigour and frogs grow wary of even slight disturbances. Search of areas of intense calling will often reveal mated pairs swimming in the water, resting in vegetation, or on the bottom. Usually a smaller male is clasping a large female tightly, waiting to release his sperm over the eggs as they emerge from the female.

In dry regions, such as the prairies and adjacent areas of central Canada, frogs and toads respond more to rain than to temperatures alone, and breed only during or immediately after extremely heavy rainfall in the spring or early summer in flooded fields, ditches and ponds. In a year when there is not a heavy rainfall they may skip that year's breeding period. All frogs and toads, east or west, in or out of the breeding season, are most active on warm rainy evenings.

To keep records, estimates should be made of the size of a breeding chorus, (i.e. numbers of calling males), together with the size of the pond, the temperatures of the air and water, and the general weather conditions (cloudy, light rain, thunderstorm, clear, etc). Counts of number of mated pairs seen, number of egg masses and their location (on the bottom, attached to vegetation, on the surface) are always useful. Later, the same pond can be revisited to record when the eggs hatch, the growth rate of tadpoles, the period they transform and the dispersal of young frogs from the breeding site.

The earliest breeders often choose ditches and spring meltwater ponds, laying their eggs early so that their tadpoles have a good chance of transforming before the pond dries up in the summer. These are also the first waters to be ice-free and which warm most rapidly in the spring. Species breeding later choose more permanent water, and the latest ones, such as the Bullfrog, choose permanent, and generally large, bodies of water. Their young usually remain tadpoles more than one year before they transform.

How far frogs will travel from the pond in which they transform, how many return in a subsequent year to breed there, how long frogs live under natural conditions, are all topics of great interest, but on which little information is available. Many Canadian species—toads, Leopard Frogs, Wood Frogs, treefrogs—spend the non-breeding period of the summer and fall in woods or meadows away from ponds.

Salamanders are more difficult to find than frogs because they do not have a breeding call that advertises their presence. Some occasionally produce sounds, but these are low "tics," apparently meant only for their immediate neighbours.

Pond-breeding salamanders generally breed early in the spring, usually at the time the first frogs are calling. On warm, rainy spring nights large numbers may be found migrating to a breeding site. Often the peak breeding period only spans a week or two. At night during this period salamanders can be observed as they crawl over the pond bottom in search of mates, or swimming to the surface for a gulp of air. Some species, particularly newts, may be quite active on sunny days, but others hide completely during daylight, and begin activity in the evening. Stream salamanders can be found under rocks at the edge of streams and rivers both in and out of water for much of the year from early spring until late fall.

The pond-breeders usually desert the egg-laying site and become terrestrial after their brief spring aquatic activity. They will seldom be found through the summer, though occasionally one will be discovered under a log, stone or similar cover in the woods, particularly after a spell of wet weather.

Salamander larvae can be sought in ponds and streams. As the summer progresses they become larger and more conspicuous. On the prairies, the Tiger Salamander larvae grow to a large size before transformation, and a careful approach to the edge of a prairie pond may reveal them in the shallows. Often the vegetation in the pond is too dense and the larvae are not evident until one sweeps the shallow repeatedly with a dip net.

Woodland salamanders can be found under logs, stones, bark and even leaf litter in or at the edge of wooded areas, particularly during wet periods. Prolonged dry weather forces them deeper, and a thorough search may prove completely fruitless in an area that abounded with salamanders after a soaking rain. These little animals will often move to the surface after dark if conditions are moist.

One can find turtles by cautiously approaching suitable basking sites in ponds, lakes, rivers and streams. Some species, the Painted Turtle being an outstanding example, will sun themselves for hours on a variety of objects such as rocks and logs. If such objects are not available they will bask on the shoreline. Turtles are very wary and quickly slip into the water if approached. Binoculars are best for checking for their presence and for observing them.

Many turtles are best observed on warm days in early spring, before any concealing vegetation has developed. Some turtles rarely bask in the open, but scanning the shallows will often reveal their heads poking above the water's surface.

All turtles lay eggs on land, and in many regions there are particularly suitable sites such as stretches of sandy shoreline, dams and road beds that numbers of females seek out each year. In late May through June and into early July, a walk along such areas in the early morning or early evening will often reveal nesting turtles, and counts of females should be tabulated for each observation period. It is best to leave a laying female undisturbed, and not to tamper with the nest, even to count the eggs. Predators such as raccoons avidly search for and dig up turtle nests, and numerous clusters of shell fragments at nesting sites attest to their efficiency. Nests can be marked by a stake placed in the ground nearby. A check of the site in the late summer, fall, or perhaps even the following spring (particularly when nesting is late and the summer cool), can reveal approximately when the eggs hatched and when the young turtles emerged.

Canadian lizards are generally active during the day, particularly on warm sunny days, but most are exceedingly wary and are rarely seen in the open. They can be found under logs and stones in suitable areas. Horned Lizards burrow into loose soil when inactive, and remain motionless, where they are almost impossible to discern.

Garter snakes and water snakes are the snake species most commonly encountered foraging in the open or basking in the sun. Although the margins of almost any body of water are good places to search for many Canadian species, garter snakes will also often be found in meadows, along fence rows and in woods. Larger species may also be encountered in the open, sunning or searching for food. Early morning and late afternoon are often the best periods in summer as some species avoid activity during the hottest portion of the day in this season, but in the cooler early spring and late fall the midday period may be the prime time to discover a snake prowling or basking. Some snakes are active on warm nights. A search for frogs on warm spring or summer nights sometimes reveals a snake bent on the same objective. Many mammal-hunting snakes also prowl on warm summer nights.

Often the most successful method of finding snakes is to turn over sun-warmed logs, flat stones, boards, pieces of metal sheeting and similar cover. Most snakes take shelter under such objects at one time or another, and the small, secretive species are rarely discovered in the open. Most of these are probably active on warm, damp nights, and their small size makes random searching for active individuals generally futile.

Snakes often den prior to winter and, particularly in northern and western areas, a favourable local site may be the autumn gathering point for hundreds, even thousands, of snakes which had dispersed for summer feeding. Dens are most often in rocky areas where cracks and crevices lead down below the frost line. Gravelly or sandy areas may provide the same situation, and even anthills have been used by wintering snakes. These sites will often have large numbers of basking snakes around them in the spring before the warm weather has dispersed emerging snakes, or in the fall when a warm day will tempt the den occupants out for one last sunbath.

All herpetologists soon learn that opportunities for observations are partly fortuitous and generally fleeting. Population numbers fluctuate: one year under particularly favourable conditions a species may be abundant, another year much less common. Amphibians and reptiles are very seasonal in activity. Emergence, breeding, and laying eggs occur in spring; hatching, feeding and growing in summer; seeking suitable wintering sites in fall; and the inactivity of hibernation, or reduced activity in aquatic sites, takes place in winter. Temperature, rainfall and type of vegetation are critical for each species and limit their possible distribution and abundance even within generally suitable areas.

In common with other animals, amphibians and reptiles produce more young in their lifetime than is necessary to replace themselves. The vast majority of these young do not survive to breed, and even fewer survive to breed twice or three times. If the hurdle of being young and small is successfully overcome, some, particularly turtles and snakes, may live and reproduce for many years. Others, the smaller kinds of frogs particularly, gain only a slight advantage in decreased vulnerability to predators as adults. They may grow beyond a size to be of interest to some predators only to become sufficiently large to be worth notice from others, and few survive to breed more than once.

Though random observations may always be of interest, systematic long-term observations are often more valuable. An observer should try and visit the same locality once a week or oftener, and record the species present, their abundance and relative activity. Above all, one should read everything available on what is known about any species that is of special interest. In this way the gaps in existing knowledge that most need to be filled are found.

Collecting and preserving amphibians and reptiles is usually left to scientists who are engaged in answering specific questions on geographic variations in appearance and life history of specific groups, species or races. Their specimens go into permanently maintained museum collections, which form an essential library available to all scientists. Preserved collections made over a hundred years ago still exist. They are often priceless for comparisons with recent collections, and sometimes are from areas which have been so altered that no kind of animal still can exist there. Collections provide the reference material for decisions on what species or races exist, and what geographic variations show the effect of past dispersal patterns or current selection pressures. These collections must also be maintained as a check on the accuracy of published accounts about them.

A conflict always exists between the need for knowledge and the potential damage to a population by removing individuals from it. The balance between these varies with each species and within each area, and the field scientist who has dedicated a life to searching for additional knowledge has the best background for weighing the need for new information against the potential harm of collecting specimens.

As a general rule, any individual that cannot be identified or one that is at least 50 km beyond its presently known range, should be preserved for positive identification and locality data. It should be sent to a museum to ensure that it is permanently available for additional study. Such specimens are best preserved in 10% formaldehyde (or formalin) or 70% ethyl alcohol, and forwarded with the collector's name, date of collection, exact locality (within distance and direction from nearest town) and any observations made on colour in life, behaviour, habitat and circumstances of capture. However, some provinces ban any collecting of certain species, and any field naturalist should be aware of current provincial laws. If collection is not possible, the next best alternative is colour photographs from several angles, or careful, detailed sketches with colour notes.

Other specimens should be measured and then released. Anyone searching for amphibians or reptiles should observe the ethics of good collectors and replace every log, board, stone or other cover that is disturbed to ensure the site remains as nearly as possible in the condition in which it was found. Often the essential aspect of such cover is the dampness maintained under it. If cover is left overturned, or carelessly replaced, this microhabitat may dry and no longer be suitable as a refuge for the animals found under it.

Studies that involve marking animals for future identification, and/or trapping animals, should only be undertaken under scientific supervision.

Literature on Amphibians and Reptiles

The following books contain both more extensive information and, usually, good lists of additional references. In addition, three major North American research journals publish extensively on amphibians and reptiles (the society that sponsors them is in brackets): *Copeia* (American Society of Ichthyologists and Herpetologists) publishes half its content on herpetology; *Herpetologica* (The Herpetologists League) and the *Journal of Herpetology* (Society for the Study of Amphibians and Reptiles) are entirely devoted to herpetology. Their current addresses are available through your library or from the Herpetology Section, National Museum of Natural Sciences. The SSAR also publishes *The Herpetological Review*, which carries a listing of recently published papers in world herpetology in most issues, *Herpetological Circulars* and the *Catalogue of American Amphibians and Reptiles*, which, when completed, will provide a summary of information and literature on each species in loose-leaf format. Over 300 individual accounts are available to date.

Textbooks and Checklists

Dowling Herndon G., and William E. Duellman. 1978. Systematic herpetology: a synopsis of families and higher categories. HISS Publications, Box 5L, 2 Washington Square Village, New York, N.Y. 10012.

Gans, Carl (Editor). 1969–1981. Biology of the Reptilia. Academic Press, New York and London. (A continuing series, now comprising nine volumes, with various co-editors).

Goin, Coleman J., Olive B. Goin, and George R. Zug. 1978. Introduction to herpetology. Third edition. W.H. Freeman and Company, San Francisco. 378 pages.

Gorham, Stanley W. 1974. Checklist of world amphibians up to January 1, 1970/Liste des amphibiens du monde d'après l'état du 1er janvier 1970. New Brunswick Museum, Saint John. 172 pages.

Noble, G. Kingsley. 1931. The biology of the Amphibia. McGraw-Hill, New York. (Dover reprint available.)

Parker, H.W., and A.G.C. Grandison. 1977. Snakes: a natural history. Second edition, revised and enlarged. British Museum (Natural History), London. 108 pages.

Porter, Kenneth R. 1972. Herpetology. W.B. Saunders, Philadelphia. 524 pages.

North American Field Guides

Behler, John L., and F. Wayne King. 1979. The Audubon Society field guide to North American reptiles and amphibians. Alfred A. Knopf, New York. 719 pages.

Conant, Roger. 1975. A field guide to reptiles and amphibians of eastern and central North America. Second edition. Houghton Mifflin, Boston. 429 pages.

Smith, Hobart M. 1978. Amphibians of North America: a guide to field identification. Golden Press, New York. 160 pages.

Smith, Hobart M., and Edmund D. Brodie, Jr. 1982. Reptiles of North America: a guide to field identification. Golden Press, New York. 240 pages.

Stebbins, Robert C. 1966. A field guide to western reptiles and amphibians: fieldmarks of all species in western North America. Houghton Mifflin, Boston. 279 pages.

Canadian Guides and Other Publications

Bleakney, J. Sherman. 1958. A zoogeographical study of the amphibians and reptiles of eastern Canada. National Museum of Canada Bulletin 155. 119 pages.

Campbell, R. Wayne, Michael G. Shepard, Brigitta M. Van Der Raay, and Patrick T. Gregory. 1982. A bibliography of Pacific Northwest herpetology. British Columbia Provincial Museum Heritage Record 14. 152 pages.

Carl, G. Clifford. 1966. The amphibians of British Columbia. Fourth edition. British Columbia Provincial Museum Handbook 2. 63 pages.

Carl, G. Clifford. 1968. The reptiles of British Columbia. Third edition. British Columbia Provincial Museum Handbook 3. 60 pages.

Cook, Francis R. 1966. A guide to the amphibians and reptiles of Saskatchewan. Saskatchewan Museum of Natural History, Popular Series 13. 40 pages.

Cook, Francis R. 1967. An analysis of the herpetofauna of Prince Edward Island. National Museum of Canada Bulletin 212. 60 pages.

Froom, Barbara. 1972. The snakes of Canada. McClelland and Stewart, Toronto. 128 pages.

Froom, Barbara. 1976. The turtles of Canada. McClelland and Stewart, Toronto. 120 pages.

Froom, Barbara. 1982. Amphibians of Canada. McClelland and Stewart, Toronto, 120 pages.

Gilhen, John. 1983. The amphibians and reptiles of Nova Scotia. Nova Scotia Museum, Halifax. In press.

Gorham, Stanley W. 1970. The amphibians and reptiles of New Brunswick. New Brunswick Museum, Saint John. 30 pages.

Hodge, Robert Parker. 1976. Amphibians and reptiles in Alaska, the Yukon and Northwest Territories. Alaska Northwest Publishing Company, Anchorage. 89 pages.

Logier, E.B.S. 1939. The reptiles of Ontario. Royal Ontario Museum Handbook 4. 63 pages. (Out of print, but perhaps available through libraries.)

Logier, E.B.S. 1952. The frogs, toads and salamanders of eastern Canada. Clark, Irwin, Toronto. 127 pages.

Logier, E.B.S. 1958. The snakes of Ontario. University of Toronto Press, Toronto. 94 pages.

Logier, E.B.S., and G.C. Toner. 1961. Checklist of the amphibians and reptiles of Canada and Alaska. Second edition. Royal Ontario Museum, Toronto. 93 pages.

Mélançon, Claude. Inconnus et méconnus (Amphibiens et reptiles de la province de Québec). Second edition. La Société zoologique de Québec Inc., Orsainville. 148 pages.

Parsons, Harold. 1976. Foul and loathsome creatures. Parks Canada, Ottawa. 59 pages. (A natural history of amphibians and reptiles in the National Parks of Ontario.)

Preston, William B. 1982. The amphibians and reptiles of Manitoba. Manitoba Museum of Man and Nature, Winnipeg. 128 pages.

In addition, may original papers dealing with Canadian herpetology appear in *The Canadian Field-Naturalist, The Blue Jay, The Canadian Journal of Zoology* and other periodicals. Recent issues should be checked.

The Canadian Amphibian and Reptile Conservation Society (CARCS) publishes a newsletter with many articles and comments on distribution, habitat, care in captivity and conservation of amphibians and reptiles in Canada. Information is available through Barbara Froom, 8 Preston Place, Toronto, Ontario M4N 2S9.

An assessment of endangered species is available in *Rare or Endangered Amphibians and Reptiles* by Francis R. Cook, pages 9 to 16 in the *Canadian Field-Naturalist*, Volume 84, Number 1, January–March issue, 1970; in *Canadian Endangered Species* by Darryl Stewart, Gage Publishing, Toronto, 1975, and in a series of six articles published as Part V, pages 115–135, in *Canada's Threatened Species and Habitats*, edited by Theodore Mosquin and Cecile Suchal, Canadian Nature Federation Special Publication No. 6, 1977. The Committee on the Status of Endangered Wildlife in Canada (COSEWIC) publishes detailed status reports and popular summary sheets of individual species. Titles to date can be obtained from the Canadian Wildlife Service, Ottawa K1A 0E7.

A comprehensive account, "Collecting and Preserving Amphibians and Reptiles" by Francis R. Cook is found as Chapter V, pages 129–141, in *Methods of Collecting and Preserving Vertebrate Animals* by R.M. Anderson, National Museum of Canada Bulletin 69, 1965, Fourth Edition, Revised.

A condensed summary of the information in this guide is available, primarily for school use, as a series of free information sheets distributed by the Information Centre, National Museum of Natural Sciences, in the series *Neotoma* [Pack-Rat] as numbers 1 – Amphibians and Reptiles; 2 – Salamanders; 3 – Frogs, Toads and Treefrogs; 4 – Turtles; 5 – Snakes and Lizards; 6 – Field Study and Conservation; 7 – Care in Captivity.

The Proper Care of Your Pet Amphibians and Reptiles

James A. Johnston

It seems that almost everyone has at one time or another kept an amphibian or reptile as a pet. Tadpoles, toads and some kinds of frogs are common favourites, which are often collected at the cottage from a local ditch or swamp. Occasionally such acquisitions extend to include turtles and snakes. This section is designed to help a child with such a pet, or a parent of a budding naturalist. The information on cages, diets and health should allow an average household to keep and maintain healthy amphibians and reptiles.

Amphibians

Frog Tadpoles and Salamander Larvae

The first step in pet care is to identify the animal you have from the previous text. If you still aren't sure, write or visit your nearest museum. Frog tadpoles and salamander larvae are very difficult to identify, but fortunately they will all do well on the same diet. Think of the challenge, to keep tadpoles or larvae healthy until transformation to discover what species of frog, toad or salamander they are.

Tadpoles and larvae are fairly easy to house. All that is required is a large bottle (4.5L in size or larger), a basin or an aquarium. It is best to set these up as you would set up an aquarium for fish. Use gravel with some rocks on the bottom, as well as some floating plants. The tadpoles and larvae will feed on these plants occasionally. A small light over the tank will help plants to grow better (Figure 1). If you use an air pump plus filter the water shouldn't need regular changing. If not, the water will have to be changed once or twice a week. Chlorinated water directly from the tap will kill your pets. However, if tap water is allowed to sit for a day or two before it is used, the chlorine will dissipate. One of the best procedures is to fill with tap water a bucket that will hold as much water as needed when you change your tank. When it is time for the next change this water will be usable.

Now that your tank is properly set up, the next question is how many occupants? For small tadpoles, a maximum of six per 4.5L is advisable, with fewer in the case of larger tadpoles such as Bullfrogs or Leopard Frogs. Avoiding crowding should help to prevent cannibalism. It is also believed that with overcrowded tadpoles, the larger ones may release hormones that retard the growth of the smaller ones.

Salamander larvae should be kept in about the same numbers per 4.5L as tadpoles. As larval salamanders get larger, however, some species can be very cannibalistic. Blue-spotted and Yellow-spotted salamanders show this behaviour but it is most common in the Tiger Salamander. When these larvae start to get bigger it is wise to keep them in separate containers.

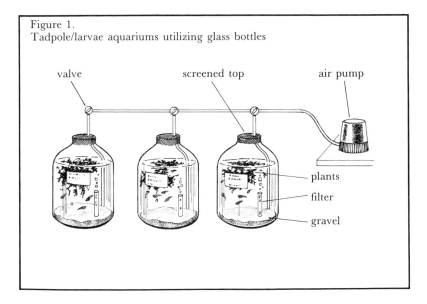

Figure 1.
Tadpole/larvae aquariums utilizing glass bottles

valve   screened top   air pump

plants
filter
gravel

In a few months you should have young frogs, toads or salamanders transforming.

Tadpoles and salamander larvae should be fed only small amounts daily. They may be fed continually on a nutritious diet of boiled romaine or escarole lettuce leaves; or they may be fed a mixed diet as long as it incorporates these lettuce varieties. The lettuce may be boiled in advance in large amounts and frozen; then small amounts can be fed daily to the tadpoles or larvae. Never leave the lettuce in for more than one day, as it will foul the water. In addition, prepared tropical fish foods, such as freeze-dried liver or shrimps, may be added once the tadpoles are more than a week old. One of the best diets is a boiled mixture of trout chow (250 gm), granular agar (20 gm), unflavoured gelatin (14 gm) and 1L of water. It should be cooled in a shallow pan and cut into cubes. These may be stored in the freezer and added to the tanks as needed. If trout chow is not available use rabbit or dog chow.

Frogs, Toads and Treefrogs

Toads and spadefoots require a container such as a small aquarium, basin or large jar of at least 4.5 to 9L in size. The best substrate for the bottom is 2 to 4 cm of fine sand (silica is the best) for the toads to burrow into. The sand should be lightly sprinkled with water every day. The top of the container should be screened for ventilation to prevent the heavy condensation which forms under a solid lid. Two or three toads per 4.5L is a maximum (Figure 2).

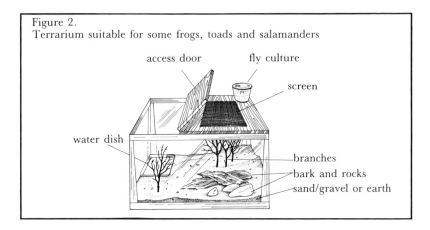

Figure 2.
Terrarium suitable for some frogs, toads and salamanders

access door fly culture screen water dish branches bark and rocks sand/gravel or earth

Treefrogs require somewhat different conditions. Using similar containers to those for toads, place a small amount of gravel, sand or earth on the bottom, anywhere from 1 to 3 cm deep. Add either small branches or potted plants to create a small forest, which will provide resting and feeding places for the treefrogs. These areas should be lightly sprinkled with water daily, but the top should be only a third to a half screen and the remainder solid glass or wood, as treefrogs do better in high humidity.

Because the true frogs prefer some standing water and because some of these frogs get fairly large, particularly the Bullfrog, Green Frog and Red-legged Frog, they will require quite spacious quarters. Use a small container for water that will occupy about one-third of the floor area inside the main holding tank. Fill the rest of the tank with gravel, sand or earth to just below the height of the water dish. Bark, small logs or rocks should be included to provide hiding places. The tank should be only half covered with screen and the remainder solid to retain some humidity. As well, the tank should be sprinkled daily (Figure 2).

For the more aquatic frogs, more water than gravel should be provided. Bullfrogs do well in an aquarium with only a large rock or shelf at the water level.

Salamanders

Keeping salamanders can provide a challenge. There are several species of stream-dwelling types, Dusky, Spring and Two-lined Salamanders, that are not recommended as pets as they need access to cold, de-clorinated water at a fairly constant temperature. The rest of the salamanders can generally be divided into terrestrial and aquatic forms. The terrestrial salamanders include the mole salamanders (family Ambystomatidae), the woodland salamanders (family Plethodontidae minus the Dusky, Spring and Two-lined Salamanders) and the eft stage of newts (family Salamandridae). For these, use a partly darkened aquarium or large jar with a small water dish and, since most terrestrial salamanders like to burrow, 5 to 7 cm of soft sandy soil. The surface of the soil can be covered with old leaves and bark to provide hiding areas. The top should be only one-third screen and the container should be sprinkled daily (Figure 2).

The aquatic salamanders include forms with external gills: the Mudpuppy, neotenous mole salamanders, and adult newts. These may be housed in conditions similar to those for their larvae. Mudpuppies might do better in water with some current in the tank (created by air stones, Figure 3). Larger rocks typical of the streams and rivers they frequent can be added. Most of these amphibians will do best if provided with an ultraviolet light source for some of the day. This can be provided by Vita-lite lamps, available in most florist supply shops. As with the larvae, adult amphibians require clean fresh water; dishes should always be kept clean and water changed twice a week.

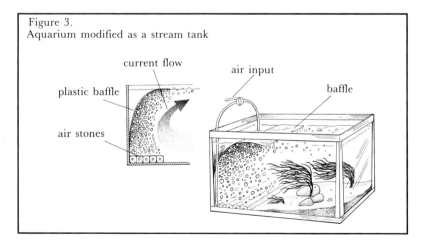

Figure 3.
Aquarium modified as a stream tank

current flow

air input

plastic baffle

baffle

air stones

Feeding in the amphibians, is basically on insects. For small, newly transformed frogs or toads, mosquitoes or fruit flies are just about right. The wingless mutant fruit flies can be cultured in special containers. Use a small, clear, half-litre-size plastic container, punch a hole in the bottom large enough to allow for the use of a pill bottle inverted with the bottom removed (Figure 4). The medium is then added, followed by several adults to lay eggs. Once the next generation of flies starts to appear, place the whole container over a matching hole in the cage top that fits the pill bottle, and remove the bottle cap. Drawn by the light, flies will gradually move out into the terrarium and provide food over several days. A number of these containers can be set up and used in rotation. However, since fruit flies are too small for larger frogs, other food sources such as crickets and mealworms, must be used. Both of these can be purchased and cultured following directions from suppliers such as pet stores. Salamanders especially, but also some toads and frogs, will welcome earthworms, which can be cultured (the smaller pink ones rather than the large red or dew worms). Bullfrogs and some other frogs will eat small mice.

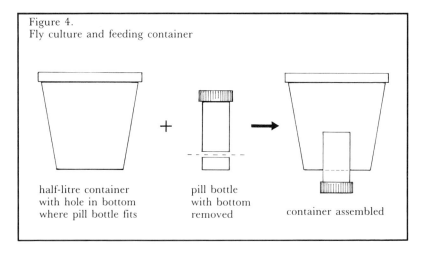

Figure 4.
Fly culture and feeding container

half-litre container
with hole in bottom
where pill bottle fits

pill bottle
with bottom
removed

container assembled

Reptiles

Turtles

With the exception of the native Wood Turtle and the introduced Box Turtle, the turtles of Canada most likely to become pets are largely aquatic. As these reptiles are of a moderate size when fully grown and need water, they require moderately large containers. Small species or single individuals may be kept in large terraria or basins, but for larger specimens a fairly large pen is best. A plastic baby bath or small wading pool are ideal, with the addition of a platform or rocks for sunning purposes (Figure 5). As turtles are not bothered by chlorinated water, a drain built into the tank is useful so that the tank can be flushed out using tap water. Chlorinated water used this way also helps prevent some infections. Be careful to use water between 15° and 25°C. A lamp should be used to heat the sunning area to between 22° and 28°C. This additional source of heat is very important to all reptiles as their digestive activity is heat-dependent and if kept at too low a temperature they will, slowly, over a period of one to two years, die of malnutrition. But beware of overheating, which can also kill them.

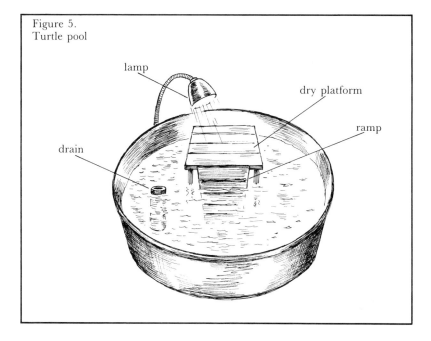

Figure 5.
Turtle pool

lamp

dry platform

ramp

drain

The more terrestrial turtles, such as the Wood Turtle, require large containers, but need only be supplied with a basin of water, at least twice the turtle's size, in one corner. A means of climbing out of the basin must also be provided. A corner for sunning should be supplied with a lamp (Figure 6).

The diets of turtles are quite varied: most aquatic turtles will readily consume earthworms, whole fish (live or fresh killed), raw meat pieces, watercress, romaine lettuce and swiss chard. These should be given in small amounts daily. Immature turtles should be given arthropods, worms and fish or meat pieces. The most terrestrial turtles are more vegetarian and do well on romaine lettuce, cabbage, berries, apples, earthworms and dog food. Never give any kind of turtle commercial turtle food, which is mainly dried ant pupae, and provides little or no nutrition and may lead to constipation. Avoid fat if meat pieces are given; hamburger contains too much and will eventually cause digestive problems. Whole animal diets provide the most natural food source, and will not lead to the vitamin deficiencies caused by feeding a continuous diet of meat or fish fillets, or hothouse lettuce. Bone meal can be added to diets of meat or fish to partly compensate for this.

Figure 6.
Terrestrial turtle or tortoise cage (using an aquarium)

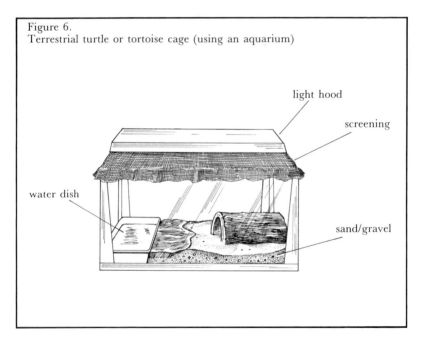

light hood

screening

water dish

sand/gravel

Snakes

All snakes can be housed the same way. Snake cages require extraordinarily secure lids as these animals are adept at escaping. You can either adapt an aquarium with a fitted lid held in place, or make a terrarium out of wood (Figure 7). The easiest to construct is a plywood box approximately 40 cm high, 40 cm wide and 53 cm long, the front of which may be glass or plastic to permit viewing. A small screened port can be added on the back, and a partially screened hinged lid fitted to the top. However, some active snakes tend to rub on screening and injure their noses. A shielded light fixture can be added in one corner. A spacious water dish is necessary as all snakes like to soak occasionally, and a hiding place should be provided. Branches may be included for the snakes to climb on. The terrarium temperature should be between 22° and 30°C with an area under the lamp 28° to 30°C. The occasional use of a sunlamp is highly beneficial. Shavings are one of the best substrates for the cage, though sand is also good; several rough rocks should be provided to aid moulting.

Snakes should be fed once every one or two weeks. Garter snakes and water snakes will do well on whole fish (live or fresh killed) worms, frogs and other amphibians. The larger snakes such

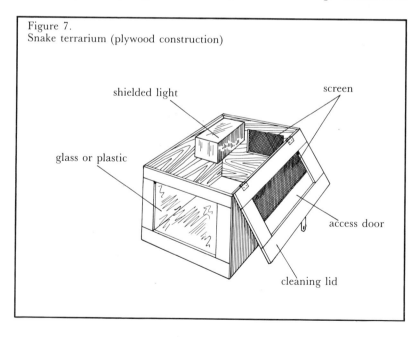

Figure 7.
Snake terrarium (plywood construction)

shielded light

screen

glass or plastic

access door

cleaning lid

as the Racers, the Fox Snake, Bullsnakes, Gopher Snakes and the Milk Snake all require rodents. These can be provided in the form of live or fresh killed whole mice, rats, gerbils or guinea pigs. These snakes will eat less frequently and need be fed only every two or three weeks. Some of the others not included in these two groups are quite specific in their food preferences and therefore can be quite difficult to keep. Species such as the Brown Snake and the Redbelly Snake eat small slugs and worms, while the Hognose Snake is particularly fond of toads but will also eat frogs. Like turtles, snakes will thrive much better on a whole animal diet. Many snakes will also grab and swallow other snakes, even individuals of their own species. Avoid keeping large and small snakes together if possible, and never feed them together as some snakes get over-excited and are most likely to grab and swallow cage mates at this time. Often this happens when two species grab opposite ends of the same food item and the larger snake continues swallowing until he has consumed not only the food but his rival as well. *Do Not attempt to keep poisonous snakes in the home*: the danger of accident or escape is too great a risk, and they should be kept only by universities, zoos, museums or similar institutions where proper security can be guaranteed.

Exotics

Cages for exotics can be quite similar to the types used for their local relations. Fine adjustments can be made after reading literature about the particular exotic you have in mind. Exotic reptiles tend most frequently to be pets, and of these, Boa Constrictors, Red-eared Turtles, Box Turtles, Caimans and Iguanas are the most common. However, many cities now have by-laws banning the keeping of these animals so check for local regulations. In addition, many of these species have been so exploited for pets, skins and other trophies that they have become increasingly rare in their native areas. Before you are tempted to purchase an exotic, remember that every one purchased means at least one *more* will be collected from the wild, and for every live one offered probably several have died from poor handling and maintenance at wholesalers. The International Convention on Trade in Endangered Species of Wild Flora and Fauna now requires export, and often import, permits before such species are allowed into the country. Animals may be seized until proof of legal importation is provided. If such animals are obtained, be certain that a full record of legal importation is provided by the seller. Further information on these regulations can be obtained from the Canadian Wildlife Service, Ottawa K1A 0E7.

Problems

Always check your snakes, turtles and lizards for ticks and mites. If any are found, coat these external parasites with 70% isopropyl alcohol, remove them with forceps, then apply methylene blue to the wound. If mites are present in your cages, move your animals to fresh clean quarters and sterilize the cages. A 0.5 cm square of Vapona "No-Pest Strip" placed in the cage will effectively kill mites.

Beware of salmonella! The best cure is prevention. Wash your hands thoroughly after handling your pets, especially turtles. This infection is caused by intestinal bacteria that are released into the water. Its general symptoms in humans can be mild to severe diarrhea. Its frequent occurrence in freshwater turtles is why Health and Welfare Canada has banned the importation of such turtles for sale in Canada.

Dietary problems should not develop if you follow the directions given. However, a once-a-month dose of multivitamins mixed in with the food is beneficial.

Anticipate health problems and check with local veterinarians to find in advance if there is anyone in your area who has knowledge or interest in amphibian or reptile treatment.

Good luck with your pet. If you treat it properly, it will be around for a long time. If you have any further problems or questions contact the museum, zoo or public aquarium nearest you.

Autobiographical Sketch

Francis Russell Cook, born 3 March 1935 at Wolfville, Nova Scotia, was the third, and last, mixed blessing to the union of a Thomas William Cook from farmering-merchant stock from Prince Edward Island, who had a Ph.D. in psychology from Yale University, and a Dorothy Clare Cochrane of United Empire Loyalist stock, who attended Acadia Ladies Seminary.

After markedly uneven progress through public and private schools in Wolfville, Toronto, Saskatoon, Victoria, and Ottawa, he finally graduated from Horton Academy in Wolfville two years before its closing, and attended Acadia University, where he obtained his B.Sc. in 1959 and his M.Sc. in 1960. His Masters dissertation was on the herpeto-fauna of Prince Edward Island, and a revised version finally appeared in 1967 as National Museum of Canada Bulletin 212.

He was an unimpressive summer-camp counsel-lor at the YMCA Camp "Y" in 1951, 1952 and 1953, and his first serious employment came in the old "museum labourer" category in the summer of 1954 when he was field and laboratory assistant to J.S. Bleakney, then Curator of Herpetology at the National Museum of Canada. After a summer (1955) participating in a field survey of amphibians, reptiles and fish with J.S. Erskine for the Nova Scotia Museum, he had matured suffi-ciently to be rehired by the National Museum as a summer assistant to

Dr. Bleakney in 1956, 1957 and 1958. In the summer of 1959, as a "technical officer," he conducted his own herpetofaunal survey (in Saskatchewan) for the National Museum. On 26 May 1960, he assumed the post vacated by Dr. Bleakney as Curator of Herpetology at the National Museum. He is now Curator, Herpetology Section, at the National Museum of Natural Sciences, National Museums of Canada. Under his direction over 24 years the Herpetology Section collections have grown from 14 000 to 98 000 specimens with emphasis on geographic and life history variation of widespread Canadian species. It is the largest amphibian and reptile collection in Canada (over two-thirds of all preserved material in these groups) and the largest collection of Canadian material in the world.

Dr. Cook spent two years on educational leave from the Museum (1968 to 1970) working with Dr. Kenneth W. Stewart in Manitoba. His thesis dissertation, an analysis of toads of the *Bufo americanus* group in a contact zone in central North America, was accepted by the University of Manitoba in 1978 for a Ph.D. degree, and published by the National Museum of Natural Sciences as Publications in Natural Sciences No. 3.

He has done field work in every province of Canada from the Maritimes to British Columbia except Newfoundland. He has also never set foot in the Yukon or the Northwest Territories. He participated in a 1967 field expedition to Jamaica for the Museum. He regards himself primarily as a herpetogeographer because he has yet to find an amphibian or reptile new to science, and his publications show an obsession with herpetofaunal distribution. He has actually finished and had published 87 papers, notes, book reviews, lists, abstracts, and miscellaneous popular articles, mostly about amphibians and reptiles, and has half again as many unfinished manuscripts or definite plans for unfinished manuscripts.

He has been a member of the Canadian Amphibian and Reptile Conservation Society since its second meeting (he missed the first) and has also belonged to the Canadian Nature Federation, the Ottawa Field-Naturalists' Club, the Nova Scotian Institute of Science, the Saskatchewan Natural History Society, the American Society of Ichthyologists and Herpetologists, the Society for the Study of Amphibians and Reptiles, and the Herpetologists League, and he was a fellow of the American Association for the Advancement of Science. He is the only person in this century to serve twice as Editor of *The Canadian Field-Naturalist* (1961 to 1966, 1981 to present) and he was also Associate Editor for herpetology from 1972 to 1980.

He is a scientific advisor for the Canadian Scientific Authority on the Convention on International Trade in Endangered Species (CITES) and is chairman of the amphibian and reptile subcommittee of the Committee On Species Endangered Within Canada (COSEWIC).

Dr. Cook is currently preparing a comprehensive technical reference on the amphibians and reptiles of Canada with emphasis on their variation, distribution, natural history, conservation and management.

He married Joyce Irma Crosby of Yarmouth, N.S., on 26 October 1962. They have two children, Wanda Jane (10 May 1964) and Thomas William (21 March 1970) and own Maplestone Farm near North Augusta in Grenville County, Ontario, where Joyce raises purebred and commercial Suffolk sheep.

Biographical Notes

Joyce Crosby Cook

Mrs. Cook has a diverse background in the biological sciences, including courses at Acadia and Carleton universities, two years as secretary to the Zoology Section at the National Museum of Canada (1958 to 1960), collection and preparation of bird and mammal specimens for the Nova Scotia Department of Lands and Forests (1961), research assistant in malacology at the National Museum of Canada (1962), laboratory demonstrator in comparative anatomy at the University of Ottawa for eight years and participation with her husband, Dr. Francis Cook, in all herpetology field work since 1963. Her first-hand familiarity with amphibian and reptile distributions throughout Canada contributed to the success of the maps she drafted for this book. She has been a full-time farmer since 1973 and is a member of the Canadian Sheep Breeders' Association and the Ontario Sheep Association.

James A. Johnston

Mr. Johnston was born in Winnipeg, Manitoba, on 1 February 1948. He received his B.Sc. from the University of Manitoba in 1971 and worked as a summer field assistant to Dr. D.W. Stewart before finishing his degree and, afterwards, as an animal-care technician at the Zoology Department, University of Manitoba. In 1972 he moved to Ottawa to become Curatorial Assistant in the Herpetology Section at the National Museum of Natural Sciences. In these jobs, he participated in field expeditions in Saskatchewan, Manitoba, Ontario and Quebec. In the laboratory, he gained wide experience keeping live amphibians and reptiles in captivity and developed a broad knowledge of the literature on this subject. These studies led to his authorship of the "Care in Captivity" section in this book. He has also developed skills in photography and has contributed photographs to numerous Canadian journals. In addition, he designed, and published on, a specialized close-up apparatus for nature photography. In 1979, he transferred to the National Museum of Science and Technology as assistant registrar, later becoming acting registrar. He has set up computerized registration procedures for the Museum's collections and has also recently completed courses for the Ontario Museums Association Certificate in Museum Studies.

Mr. Johnston married Linda Davighnon, also of Winnipeg, in 1971 and they have two children: Michelle, born in 1975; and Jamie, born in 1980. Linda is Budget Control Officer for Publications with the Canada Mortgage and Housing Corporation.

Charles H. Douglas

Charles H. Douglas was born near Aberdeen, Scotland, 28 December 1925 and moved to Canada when he was five. His father was a golf professional at Trenton (1928 to 1932) and at Cornwall (1932 to 1945), and Charles attended Cornwall Collegiate and Vocational School. He became an apprentice draftsman with Courtauld Canada Ltd. in Cornwall after leaving school and spent three years serving in England with the Royal Canadian Air Force. He was discharged in 1945 with the rank of Sergeant Bombardier. Upon return to civilian life, he held a variety of jobs in finance, car sales and real estate while doing as much free-lance commercial art as he could, before finally deciding to make the latter aptitude a permanent rather than a part-time vocation. In 1966, he won appointment to his present position as Zoological Illustrator with the National Museum of Natural Sciences. He has contributed to a legion of technical and popular publications published by Museum staff, including *The Freshwater Molluscs of Canada, A Guide to the Freshwater Sport Fishes of Canada, The Mammals of Canada*, and the *Handbook of Canadian Mammals* series. He conceived the very successful *Natural History Notebook* series, for which he prepared all the illustrations and much of the text. This series ran in newspapers throughout Canada in both English and French, and has been published by the Museum in five volumes containing 52 accounts each.

Mr. Douglas married Jeannine Morin of Timmins in 1951 and they have three children: Brian, born in 1952, James in 1953, and William in 1961. They are also the proud grandparents of Robin, born in 1981. Jeannine works for the Department of Communications.